MASS SPECTROMETRIC ANALYSIS OF SOLIDS

MASS SPECTROMETRIC ANALYSIS OF SOLIDS

Edited by

ARTHUR J. AHEARN

Member of Technical Staff, Bell Telephone Laboratories, Inc.
Murray Hill, New Jersey, U.S.A.

ELSEVIER PUBLISHING COMPANY

AMSTERDAM - LONDON - NEW YORK

1966

ELSEVIER PUBLISHING COMPANY
335 JAN VAN GALENSTRAAT, P.O. BOX 211, AMSTERDAM

AMERICAN ELSEVIER PUBLISHING COMPANY, INC.
52 VANDERBILT AVENUE, NEW YORK, N.Y. 10017

ELSEVIER PUBLISHING COMPANY LIMITED
RIPPLESIDE COMMERCIAL ESTATE, RIPPLE ROAD, BARKING, ESSEX

LIBRARY OF CONGRESS CATALOG CARD NUMBER 66-16715

WITH 46 ILLUSTRATIONS AND 13 TABLES

PRINTED IN THE NETHERLANDS

Preface

The great increase in solid state physics after 1945 stimulated the development of new analytical techniques for the determination of the chemical composition of materials. The purpose of this book is to describe one of these—a mass spectrometric technique.

Although it is new, it is already productive and is being developed rapidly by many scientists. For several reasons, it seemed appropriate to have individuals actively engaged in this particular technique write chapters to cover those areas for which they are particularly qualified.

February, 1966 ARTHUR J. AHEARN

Contents

CHAPTER I

Introductory Survey

A. J. AHEARN
Bell Telephone Laboratories, Inc., Murray Hill, N.J.

1. INTRODUCTION

The great increase in solid state physics—both pure and applied—after 1945 stimulated the development of new analytical techniques for the determination of the chemical composition of materials. In most cases, the particular need was to detect and identify impurities at low concentrations, first in the parts per million (ppm) range and before long in the parts per billion (ppb) range.

The needs of semiconductor technology furnished the principal stimulant for the initial development of one of these new analytical techniques. For example, the presence of 10 ppb of copper [1] in germanium or 2 ppb of gold [2] in silicon is reflected in the electrical properties of these semiconductors.

However there are many other areas in the physics and chemistry of solids where properties are markedly affected by impurities when present in the low ppm region. When its impurity content is reduced below 10 ppm, tungsten [3] is readily machinable whereas at the 200 ppm level it is brittle and difficult to work. When beryllium[4] is purified to a few ppm, a 40-fold increase in ductility results. As little as 2 ppm of boron in graphite[5] adversely affects its efficiency in a nuclear reactor. The presence of a few ppm of silver in lead will reduce the velocity of a crystal grain boundary migration by a factor of one thousand[6].

These represent only a few typical examples of many specific cases of solid state properties reviewed elsewhere[7] that are vastly affected by impurities in the ppm and ppb range. This is the concentration range in which this new technique—spark source mass spectrometry of solids—is almost ideally suited to make a

References p. 14

valuable contribution by identifying the specific elements involved and by setting better than order of magnitude values for their concentrations.

Any mass spectrometer consists essentially of three components which must be housed in a highly evacuated container. The first is the source for ionizing the sample under study. Ion sources in mass spectrometry usually supply positive ions, but sometimes negative ion sources are used. The second component is an analyzer to separate these ions according to their mass/charge ratio. These analyzers usually consist of a combination of electric and magnetic fields. The third component is a detector to record the position and intensity of the various ion beams in the mass/charge spectrum. This is done electrically or photographically. The term spectrograph indicates the use of photographic detection. In the past, the term spectrometer was reserved for electrical detection. However, the term mass spectrometry is now the generally accepted designation for this mass analysis technique regardless of the type of detection employed.

The mass/charge ratio of the ion determines the position of the ion beam in the recorded spectrum. Consequently, the mass/charge ratios can be calculated from these positions. When the ion source supplies only singly charged ions, a mass/charge spectrum is equivalent to a mass spectrum. When multiply charged ions are also supplied, the spectrum can still be treated as a mass spectrum since the multiply charged ions have an integral number of electronic charges.

In this introductory chapter, the author will briefly describe this spark source mass spectrometric technique, indicate its capabilities and limitations, outline those problems which can be solved by this method, and suggest areas where this technique can help to improve the properties of solids that are influenced by impurities. An attempt will be made to give the reader and potential user of this technique a realistic picture of the field in its present state of development. The areas covered by subsequent chapters will merely be introduced and the reader will be referred to the chapter in question.

2. HISTORY

Mass spectrometric techniques have been used many times in the past for special analytical studies of solids. Impurities in metals and semiconductors have been measured by vaporizing the sample into an electron bombardment* type positive ion source. Isotopic dilution techniques with thermal ionization* sources and electron bombardment sources have been used to achieve very high detection sensitivities for specific elements. Surface studies have utilized ions produced by ion bombardment (sputtering).*

The mass spectrometric technique emphasized in this book employs the vacuum spark source of positive ions. Here a radio frequency (about one megacycle) voltage of several tens of kilovolts is applied in pulses across a small gap (a few thousandths of a centimeter) between two electrodes of the sample in a vacuum. The vacuum breakdown that occurs in this gap initiates an electrical vacuum discharge. The positive ions from this discharge can be used to analyze nearly all inorganic solids.

DEMPSTER first demonstrated the possibilities of the spark source for mass spectrometric work in 1934[8]. During World War II he and his associates used this source in mass spectrographic studies[9] which suggested that this analytical combination might be not only a very sensitive technique but also one of broad applicability. These early expectations have been amply fulfilled.

SHAW AND RALL[10] in 1947 reported the design and construction of a spark source mass spectrograph for analytical work but included no results.

The next use of the spark source in mass spectrometry was by GORMAN, JONES AND HIPPLE[11] in 1951. Unlike DEMPSTER's pioneering studies where photographic detection was employed, they used electrical detection and demonstrated with standard samples that the method could be made quantitative.

HANNAY chose the spark type source for general analytical work on the expectation that it should be relatively nonselective, *i.e.*,

* These and other ion sources are treated in detail in Ch. II.

References p. 14

all elements should have about the same detection sensitivity, and a substantial gain in sensitivity over current analytical techniques should be achieved with the best available photographic plates. In order to record all masses simultaneously for samples of unknown composition, he designed and built a mass spectrograph using the MATTAUCH AND HERZOG geometry of double-focusing described in Section 3 to be used with a pulsed radio frequency spark source[12]. With this instrument HANNAY AND AHEARN[13] demonstrated that impurity concentrations at least as low as 0.1 ppm could be detected, that the mass spectrographic values were directly proportional to the concentration over a wide range, and that the detection sensitivity was approximately the same for all elements tested.

The next step in the development of this analytical technique began about 1958 when commercial mass spectrographs for solids analysis first became available. A list of such instruments on the market today includes the MS-7 by Associated Electrical Industries, Manchester, England; the 21-110 by Consolidated Electrodynamics Corporation, Pasadena, Calif.; the GRAF-2 by Nuclide Analysis Associates, University Park, Penna.; the Atlas SM-1 by Atlas Mess und Analysentechnik GmbH, Bremen, Germany; and the JMS-010 by JEOLCO (Japan Electron Optical Laboratory Company), Medford, Mass.

All of these use the same general type of pulsed radio frequency spark source. They all are designed primarily for photographic detection. They are all designed for general analytical work and therefore employ the MATTAUCH AND HERZOG geometry of double-focusing described in Section 3.

3. EQUIPMENT

Chapter II presents in detail the properties and performance of positive ion sources with particular emphasis on the radio frequency spark and discharge type sources.

Because it is relatively nonselective among the elements, the radio-frequency spark source is being widely used in spite of the wide energy spread of the ions, the erratic nature of the spark and the fluctuating character of the ion current supplied. The wide energy spread of the ions necessitates the use of a double-focusing instrument, *i.e.*, one that focuses ions that are divergent in direction as well as dispersed in velocity. The fluctuating character of the ion current practically dictates that if electrical detection is employed it must be a measurement of the ratio of the mass analyzed ion beam to the total beam entering the mass analyzer. The alternative is to use an integrating detector. In practice an integrator in the form of a photographic plate is almost exclusively used at present.

In the earlier work of GORMAN *et al.*[11], electrical detection was used for the quantitative determination of elements present at concentrations of about 1% which correspond to currents of 10^{-12} A. If the full capabilities of present-day mass spectrographs[14] were to be realized with electrical recording, it would be necessary to measure quantitatively currents of 10^{-19} A, while circumventing the fluctuating character of this current.

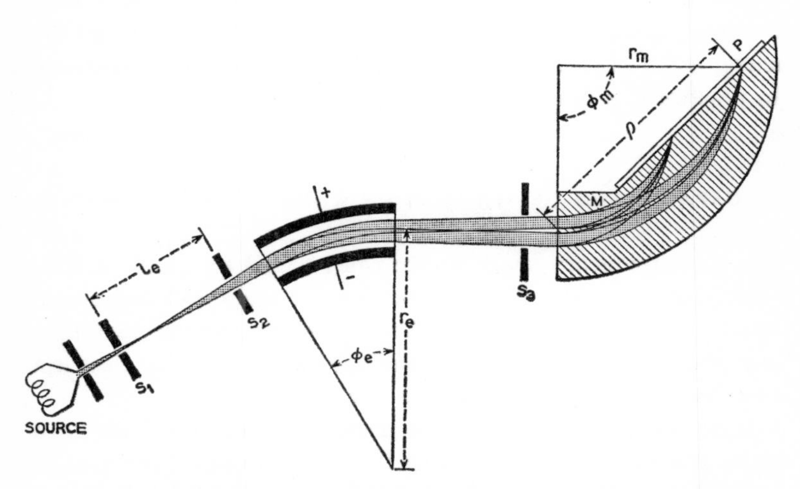

Fig 1. Double focusing in a Mattauch and Herzog type mass spectograph. (N. B. HANNAY, *Science*, 134 (1961) 1220).

References p. 14

If the spark source instrument with photographic recording is to be satisfactory for general analytical work, then substantially the entire mass range of the periodic table of elements must be recorded in focus. This dictates the MATTAUCH–HERZOG[15,16,17] geometry of double-focusing in which ions of any given mass/charge ratio in a divergent beam which is inhomogeneous in energy are simultaneously direction and velocity focused at a specific plane at the exit end of the magnetic analyzer, as shown in Fig. 1.

Consider any two ion trajectories such as the two that define the angular divergence of the beam. In each trajectory consider only ions of two masses m_1 and m_2 and two energies E_1 and E_2. The trajectories of these ions are sketched in Fig. 1. Emerging from the electrostatic analyzer are two nondivergent beams; one contains the ions of energy E_1 while the other contains those of E_2. Mass analysis occurs in the magnetic analyzer where simultaneously the ion paths of each mass are focused on the indicated plane at its output. This focusing occurs because the dispersion of the two mono-energetic beams compensates for the angular divergence between them.

Just as the angular divergence of the beam needs to be limited to an appropriately low value by the apertures S_1 and S_2, so the energy band must be correspondingly limited by the S_3 aperture. In practice it is limited to a few hundred electron volts.

4. CAPABILITIES OF SPARK SOURCE MASS SPECTROMETRY

The radio-frequency spark source can be used to sample a wide variety of materials. With conductors the spark can be formed directly between electrodes of the sample. This simple technique can also be used with a semiconductor even when its electrical resistivity is at least as high as a few hundred Ω cm.

It is possible to make an electrical insulator contribute to a spark and a number of techniques for doing this have been used.

Frequently, samples are presented for analysis in powder form. Solid rods suitable for sparking can be formed either by sintering or by compacting the sample with a suitably pure binding material. A number of such techniques for handling powdered samples of metals, semiconductors and insulators have been developed.

When the sample is in liquid form, an otherwise clean surface of a suitably pure material is contaminated with the liquid or a wet sludge of a suitable powder is made into a dried compacted electrode. These techniques are discussed later.

When there is sufficient sample which can be readily cut or machined, it is best to shape the electrodes into two rods about 20 mm long and 2 or 3 mm in diameter. However, there are techniques for testing samples from solid state devices and from crystal growing set-ups that are small enough to justify the term microsamples. All of these special sample techniques are described in Chapter IV.

Thus the radio frequency spark is capable of sampling a wide variety of materials—metals, semiconductors and insulators in the form of solids, liquids or powders. Usually it is employed to detect elements at low concentrations as discussed in the following paragraphs. However, it is sometimes used for relatively high concentrations when the total sample available is too small to examine by other analytical methods.

The high detection sensitivity and the approximate absence of selectivity from element to element is a most useful feature of the spark source mass spectrograph. With a few exceptions discussed later, all elements in the periodic table can be detected at concentrations in the neighborhood of a part-per-billion (ppb) atomic fraction[14]. The exact detection sensitivity depends on many factors including the mass of the element in question and the kinetic energy of the positive ion that activates the photographic plate. These characteristics, as well as the detection sensitivity in terms of sample consumption and in terms of sample and impurity amounts needed for detection at the photographic plate, are treated in Chapters II and III.

Basically, the detection sensitivity of a given experimental setup is determined by the weakest mass line on the photographic plate that the analyst can visually or instrumentally detect. This is a

References p. 14

signal to noise problem where in this case the noise is the diffuse background on the emulsion against which the mass line must be detected. The problem of background lines will be discussed later. By increasing the exposure, elements of increasingly lower concentration will be revealed by their mass lines, but an exposure limit is always reached beyond which the increase in background shields lower concentrations from detection[13]. With modern commercial instruments this limit is about one microcoulomb per exposure on the photographic plate.

In addition to the intrinsic background of the photographic emulsion itself, there are two factors contributing diffuse background. Some of the ions in transit will be scattered from the original beam by collisions with residual gas molecules and at edges of beam-limiting apertures. Scattering from gas atoms is probably the more important factor of the two. Ions scattered in transit through the magnetic analyzer have a fair probability of reaching and activating the emulsion.

Of particular interest are those ions that undergo a charge transfer in a collision with a residual gas atom picking up one or more electrons. Charge transfers from $+2$ to $+1$, $+3$ to $+2$, and $+4$ to $+3$ are frequently revealed by rather sharply terminated bands of diffuse background. These bands extend from $m/2$ to $2m$, $m/3$ to $3m/4$ and from $m/4$ to $4m/9$ respectively, m representing the mass/charge value for the singly charged ion in question. The terminal points correspond to charge transfers that occurred at the photographic plate and at the entrance to the magnetic analyzer respectively.

To minimize the effects of scattering, high vacuum techniques such as metal gasket seals, high speed pumping, and outgassing by baking[18] are employed.

When the 20 keV ions in a spark source mass spectrograph strike the photographic emulsion, they produce not only a mass line spectrum but also one or more of the following secondary products: X-rays, luminescence, negative ions, secondary electrons and reflected positive ions, all of which can fog the emulsion. The negative ions and secondary electrons would be returned to the low mass side of the incident ion by the magnetic field. The reflected positive ions would be returned on the high mass side. The X-rays and luminescence would be distributed about the incident ion and probably extend beyond the limitation in mass line length imposed by the magnet gap.

The fogging produced by major component ions is appreciable when the integrated ion charge is sufficient to record an element in the ppb region. It can be partially suppressed by shielding the emulsion from these ions with a metal mask[12] but more successfully by removing that segment of the plate where the major component ions would otherwise be incident. With an appropriate aperture in the plate holder, these ions and their secondary products can be trapped in a Faraday collector[19, 27].

An element that appears in a mass spectrum may come from the sample or it may be instrument background. However, with a few exceptions, when the concentration of an element in a sample is less than its detection sensitivity of about 1 ppb[14], the element is not detected. This sets an upper limit of about 1 ppb for the contribution of most elements from the instrument background. The principal exceptions are hydrogen, carbon, nitrogen, oxygen and their products. The minimum observed for these elements is in the low ppm region. All of the materials tested may have contained these elements at this level but it is more likely that they are instrument background. That being the case the sensitivity for detection of these elements is correspondingly limited to the low ppm region. Another exception to this upper limit of about 1 ppb from instrument background consists of element mass lines from materials, other than the sample in the spark chamber, that sometimes are recorded. These ions are either of the material itself or are memory effects from inadequately cleaned surfaces.

Mass line background is sometimes introduced by hydrocarbons[12] of unknown origin. The resolving power usually available is frequently adequate to separate the hydrocarbon mass lines from those of elements of the same nominal mass thereby circumventing this background limitation.

The radio-frequency spark source produces ions with positive

References p. 14

charges from one to several electronic units as well as singly-charged molecular species. In the case of graphite[20], ion species containing as many as 30 carbon atoms have been recorded.

Molecules consisting of oxides, hydrides, hydroxides and carbides have appeared in mass spectra with this source. In addition complex molecular ions[21, 22] like Al_2Cr, GaP_2 and Ga_2As have been observed.

Multiply charged ions, molecular species and complex molecules yield mass lines of the same nominal mass as many elements. The detection of these elements is thus inhibited by this masking since the available resolving power is frequently inadequate to resolve lines of the same nominal mass[23]. This limitation is circumvented only at the sacrifice of some sensitivity. For polyisotopic elements, a lower abundance isotope that is not masked can sometimes be used for identification and quantitative determination. For mono-isotopic elements, the only recourse is to use a multiply charged ion for detection. Multiply charged ions of molecular species and complex molecules are not usually detected. Apparently dissociation is more probable than the loss of a second electron. The masking by multiply charged ions of other elements in the sample can usually be circumvented by resorting to not more than the doubly or triply charged ion of this monoisotopic element. Since the ion intensity decreases by a factor as high as ten for each additional electron removed, resorting to multiply charged ions for detection becomes costly in sensitivity loss.

The Bell Telephone Laboratories mass spectrograph[12] was calibrated by means of standard samples in the form of semi-conductors doped with known impurities in the concentration range 10^{-4} to 10^{-7}. Fig. 2 shows the calibration obtained with such a series of germanium samples doped with known concentrations of antimony[13]. The scatter in the data of Fig. 2 indicates an uncertainty factor of about 2. Since this work, the techniques for quantitative analysis by photographic recording in this field have been refined substantially. This subject is treated in detail in Chapter III.

Early work with standard samples gave "order of magnitude"

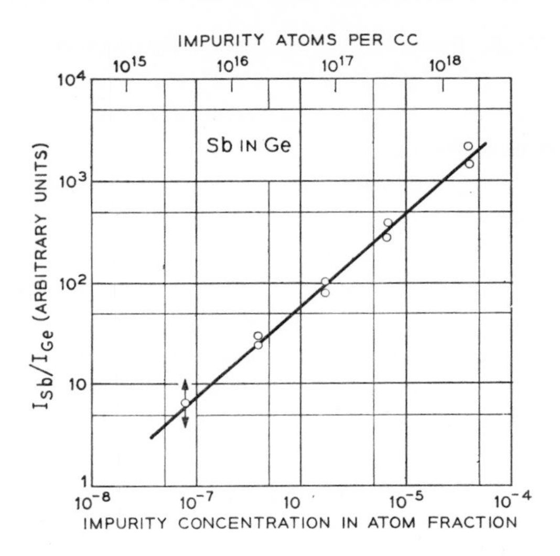

Fig. 2. Mass spectrometric measurements of antimony in germanium standard samples that are based on electrical measurements. (N. B. HANNAY AND A. J. AHEARN, *Anal. Chem.*, 26 (1954) 1056.)

agreement with their known composition and this was accepted as the degree of precision attainable at the time. In 1951, GORMAN, JONES AND HIPPLE[11] analyzed standard samples and achieved excellent precision with electrical detection. However, for some components of the standard their mass spectrometric determination disagreed significantly with the established composition. This discrepancy indicated that the intensities of some of the ion beams arriving at the detector were not representative of the composition of the electrodes participating in the spark. The ratio of the mass-spectrometric concentration to the accepted concentration gave them Relative Sensitivity Coefficient (RSC) values for the elements comprising the standard. When they analyzed other standards with the same components, they obtained excellent agreement with the known composition after their mass spectrometric determinations were corrected by these RSC values. This general subject of the degree with which the ions presented to the detector represent the composition of the sample is treated in Chapter II.

References p. 14

5. TYPICAL ANALYTICAL PROBLEMS

In order to illustrate the ways in which this analytical tool can be used, let us consider the kinds of problem to which it can furnish an answer. Sometimes one wants to know whether a specific element is present in a given sample but more frequently a complete list of the elements present is requested. The spark source double-focusing mass spectrograph is ideally suited to answer this type of question. Since the developed photographic plate will record all elements, not only will this specific element be revealed if present but in addition unsuspected elements may be disclosed. Invariably the concentration of a detected element needs to be known. This need usually can be met satisfactorily with order of magnitude concentration obtained by a visual examination of the plate, provided the customary graded series of exposures has been made. By inspection, the exposures are identified at which the major component and the trace impurity have mass lines of the same optical transmission. When they are monoisotopic elements the impurity concentration is approximately equal to the inverse ratio of these exposures.

Very frequently the concentration of a specific element or of impurities in general is to be compared in two or more samples. This was accomplished by mounting two sets of samples (each consisting of two electrodes) in the HANNAY instrument[12] and recording the mass spectra of each on the same plate under the same background conditions of vacuum, etc. This system is frequently used with today's commercial instruments. By making closely graded exposures of each sample, a fairly precise estimate of the relative concentrations of specific elements can be made.

Often the analytical studies requested demand better than order of magnitude accuracy. This requires a carefully graded series of exposures which extend down to about 10^{-13} C in order to record the major component mass lines in the usable part of the plate response curve. With microphotometric measurements, concentrations for many elements can be determined to within a factor of about three without knowledge of the Relative Sensitivity

Coefficients for the elements in question in the specific sample.

Standard samples appropriate to the low concentrations that can be detected by this technique are rare. Germanium samples containing antimony in the concentration range 0.1 to 40 ppm shown in Fig. 2 and silicon containing boron in the range 0.1 to 200 ppm[13] are typical of semiconductors that have been doped with selected elements the concentrations of which can be established from electrical measurements.

With the present technology of silicon and germanium and perhaps other semiconductors, selected elements can be doped into these matrices in the ppb range and the concentrations therein of these elements unambiguously determined[24].

Another type of standard sample is a dilute solution of selected polyisotopic elements in appropriate matrices. The selected elements need to have one or more isotopes of very low abundance. One such standard sample that has been successfully used in the ppb region[23] is a 0.019% solution of platinum in gold. This quantity is readily determined by spectrochemical techniques which also indicate that the sample is homogeneous. The platinum-190 isotope has an abundance of 0.0127%. Consequently, the concentration of this isotope in the gold was 24 ppb atomic fraction.

When a standard sample is available or its equivalent in terms of reliable RSC values is at hand, quantitative determinations with a standard deviation of about 30% are achievable. This general problem is treated in Chapters II and III.

Throughout this chapter and particularly in this discussion of types of analytical problems, sample homogeneity has been assumed. But the sample consumption is small—about 0.1 mg[25] for detection of elements at 1 ppm—compared with the emission spectroscopic technique where in the above case the sample consumed would be greater by a factor of about one hundred. Consequently the homogeneity requirements are correspondingly more stringent in this mass spectrometric technique.

On the other hand this technique is well suited to studies of a particular class of inhomogeneity, namely surface contamination, which is very important in semiconductor physics. Sometimes it is

References p. 14

this surface contamination *per se* that is the problem[13]; at other times the surface sensing ability of this technique is employed to study liquids or contamination sources[26]. Surface contamination studies are treated in detail in Chapters IV and V.

The spark source technique is also developing into a powerful tool as a microprobe for studying small scale inhomogeneities. It can be used to study not only inhomogeneities directionally over the surface of a specimen but also the compostion of surface films in depth independent of the substrate. These microprobe techniques which are described in Chapter 5, probably will profitably supplement the electron microprobe in some analytical studies of surfaces in the future.

REFERENCES

1 W. P. Slichter and E. D. Kolb, *Phys. Rev.*, 87 (1952) 527.
2 G. Bemski and J. D. Struthers, *J. Electrochem. Soc.*, 105 (1958) 588.
3 *Ultra High Purity Metals*, American Society for Metals, Metals Park, Ohio, 1962.
4 B. Schaub and G. Cabane, *Compt. Rend.*, 257 (1963) 444.
5 H. H. Hausner and S. B. Roboff, *Materials for Nuclear Reactors*, Reinhold, New York, 1955.
6 J. W. Rutter and K. T. Aust, *Trans. Met. Soc., A.I.M.E.*, 218 (1960) 682.
7 G. H. Morrison (Editor), *Trace Analysis, Physical Methods*, Wiley, New York, 1965; W. G. Pfann, *Zone Melting*, Wiley, New York, 1965.
8 A. J. Dempster, *Proc. Am. Phil. Soc.*, 75 (1935) 755; *Rev. Sci. Instr.*, 7 (1936) 46.
9 A. J. Dempster, *MDDC 370*, U.S. Dept. of Commerce, 1946.
10 A. E. Shaw and W. Rall, *Rev. Sci. Instr.*, 18 (1947) 278.
11 J. G. Gorman, E. J. Jones and J. A. Hipple, *Anal. Chem.*, 23 (1951) 438.
12 N. B. Hannay, *Rev. Sci. Instr.*, 25 (1954) 644.
13 N. B. Hannay and A. J. Ahearn, *Anal. Chem.*, 26 (1954) 1056.
14 N. B. Hannay, *Science*, 134 (1961) 1220.
15 R. Herzog, *Z. Physik*, 89 (1934) 447.
16 J. Mattauch and R. Herzog, *Z. Physik*, 89 (1934) 786.

17 J. Mattauch, *Phys. Rev.*, 50 (1936) 617.
18 R. M. Elliott, R. D. Craig and G. A. Errock, in H. von Koch and G. Lyungberg (Editors), *Instruments and Measurements*, Vol. 1, Academic Press, New York, 1961, p. 271.
19 A. J. Ahearn and D. L. Malm, *Appl. Spectry.*, 20 (1966).
20 E. Dornenburg and H. Hintenberger, *Z. Naturforsch.*, 14a (1959) 767.
21 R. D. Craig, G. A. Errock and J. D. Waldron, in J. D. Waldron (Editor), *Advances in Mass Spectrometry*, Pergamon, New York, 1959, p. 136.
22 A. J. Ahearn and C. D. Thurmond, *J. Phys. Chem.*, 66 (1962) 575.
23 A. J. Ahearn, *11th Annual Meeting on Mass Spectrometry and Allied Topics*, San Francisco, 1963.
24 Dow Corning Corporation, private communication, 1964.
25 J. S. Halliday, P. Swift and W. A. Wolstenholme, *Conference on Mass Spectrometry*, Paris, 1964.
26 F. G. Allen, T. M. Buck and J. T. Law, *J. Appl. Phys.*, 31 (1960) 979.
27 H. Mai, *J. Sci. Instrum.*, 47 (1965) 339.

CHAPTER II

The Production of Ions from Solids

RICHARD E. HONIG
RCA Laboratories, Princeton, N.J.

1. INTRODUCTION

To analyze solids by mass spectrometry, the sample material must be vaporized and ionized, preferably in such a way that the composition of the ionized vapor represents accurately that of the solid. Some of the methods used today were described already in early papers by DEMPSTER[1], others have been developed more recently. This Chapter outlines the major methods used to produce positive ions from solids, and presents the operational details of various vacuum discharge sources. The discussion applies primarily to *inorganic* solids in elemental or compound form, which often contain impurities at the parts per billion (ppb) level. The final Section discusses various parameters, in particular the efficiency of ion production and sensitivities, which affect the fidelity with which the ions arriving at the mass spectrometer detector represent the composition of the solid sample.

2. ION SOURCES

To survey the different types of ion sources, it is useful to classify them according to the method of ion production, even if this classification is of necessity a subjective matter. Table I shows the five major methods used today for the production of ions from solids, and quotes for each source the following important characteristics:

(1) width ΔV, in volts, of the ion energy distribution;

(2) the most suitable type of mass analyzer;
(3) distribution among major charged species;
(4) coverage, as defined below;
(5) the most suitable type of detector.

TABLE I

SURVEY OF ION SOURCES

Method	ΔV (V)	Mass analyzer	Charge distribution			Coverage	Detector
			1+	2+	3+		
Direct Heating							
Thermal ions	10^{-1}	SF	S	—	—	Selective	Electric
Neutral vapor ionized by electron impact	10^{-1}	SF	S	W	—	Wide	Electric
Electron Bombardment	10^{2}	DF	S	M	W	Wide	Electric
Focused Radiation							
Arc image furnace: neutrals	10^{-1}	SF	S	W	—	Wide	Electric
Laser source							
Thermal ions	10^{0}	SF	S	—	—	Interm.	Plate
Neutral vapor ionized in arc	10^{2}	DF	S	S	M	Wide	Plate
Ion Bombardment							
Secondary ions	10^{1}	SF/DF	S	—	—	Interm.	Electric
Neutral vapor ionized by electron impact	10^{0}	SF	S	W	—	Wide	Electric
Vacuum Discharges							
r.f. spark	10^{3}	DF	S	M	W	Wide	Plate
Vibrating arc	10^{2}	DF	S	S	M	Wide	Plate
Pulsed d.c. arc	10^{2}	DF	S	S	M	Wide	Plate

SF = single focusing; DF = double focusing.
S = strong; M = medium; W = weak.

References p. 53

The magnitude of ΔV determines what type of instrument is required for mass analysis. Ions with $\Delta V < 10$ V can be mass-analyzed in a simple magnetic filter, while $\Delta V > 10$ V necessitates the use of a double-focusing machine. The relative concentrations of singly- and multiply-charged species shown in the charge distribution columns indicate the character of the mass spectra. For maximum simplicity and minimum interference, a spectrum consisting solely of singly-charged species would be preferable, but this is obtainable only in conjunction with an undesirably strong selectivity. The data given in the coverage column indicate qualitatively relative sensitivities of individual components: for "wide coverage", all elemental sensitivities lie within a factor of three, while for the "selective" case they may differ by many orders of magnitude. The last column quotes the detector most suitable for use in conjunction with a given source. In the following, the various methods listed in Table I will be discussed in detail.

a. *Direct Heating*

Since these methods produce ions with thermal energy spreads of less than 0.3 eV, a simple magnetic filter is adequate for mass analysis.

(i) Thermal ions

When a surface is heated in a vacuum, most of the particles vaporized from it will have no charge, but a certain fraction, depending on conditions, will come off as positive and/or negative ions. The method of thermal ionization has been the subject of several recent reviews, *e.g.* by WILSON AND DALY[2], and by WEBSTER[3], and will therefore be discussed only briefly. The basic process is described by the LANGMUIR–SAHA equation[4] for positive ions:

$$I^{+}/A = \exp\left(e\,(W - IP)/kT\right) = \exp\left(11606(W - IP)/T\right) \qquad (1)$$

and for negative ions:

$$I^{-}/A = \exp\left(e\,(EA - W)/kT\right) = \exp\left(11606(EA - W)/T\right) \qquad (2)$$

where, for the element in question,

I^+ = number of positive ions
A = number of neutrals
I^- = number of negative ions
e = electronic charge = $1.6021 \cdot 10^{-19}$ C
W = work function of surface, in electron-volts (eV)
IP = ionization potential, in eV
EA = electron affinity, in eV
k = the Boltzmann constant = $1.3804 \cdot 10^{-23}$ J/°
T = temperature of hot surface, in °K.

It is clear from eqs. (1) and (2) that elements with a low ionization potential will be emitted largely as positive ions, while for elements with high electron affinity the production of negative ions is very efficient. For the case that $IP > W$, or $EA < W$, it is evidently advantageous to operate at the highest temperature possible, in order to enhance the emission, respectively, of positive ions or negative ions. This consideration led to the development of the multiple-filament source[5] in which the first filament is heated to the temperature best suited to vaporize the material under study, while the second filament is run at the highest practical temperature to ionize the particles emitted by the first. To avoid excessive vaporization of the ionizing filament, its temperature should be kept below 2800°K. More recently, a thermal ion source was developed by VOSHAGE AND HINTENBERGER[6], which combines the advantage of the multiple-filament system with the efficiency of a double furnace that is completely enclosed except for the exit slit. The charge of material to be studied is vaporized at one end, at an appropriate temperature produced by external electron bombardment, and diffuses to the other end where it is ionized at a surface kept at a very high temperature.

Singly-charged positive ions are obtained by this method from elements with ionization potentials below about 9 eV, *i.e.* from two thirds of the periodic table. Similarly, negative ions are formed from elements with an electron affinity > 1 eV. Because of the exponential character of eqs. (1) and (2), the sensitivities of

References p. 53

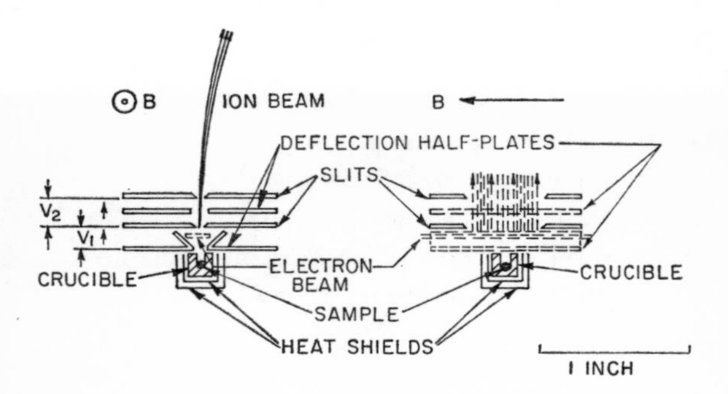

Fig. 1. Geometry of electron impact source.
$V_1 \approx 20$ V; $V_2 \approx 1000$ V

individual species will vary over many orders of magnitude, which results in strong selectivity.

(ii) Neutral vapor ionized by electron impact

This well-known method, generally used in gas analysis, can be applied to solids by the addition of a crucible which is heated electrically to suitable temperatures. If it is desired to maximize the concentration of neutrals vaporized in the ionization region[7], and thereby the detection sensitivity, a source geometry such as shown in Fig. 1 is chosen, but two other orientations are possible. HICKAM[8] analyzed Cu samples for Ag impurities with this method, while the present author[9] studied semiconductors with the source geometry shown in Fig. 1. To perform meaningful analyses with this system, the sample must be completely vaporized and ion currents integrated over time, in order to eliminate the effects of vapor pressure differences. Furthermore, the crucible material must be chosen with care so as to minimize reactions between sample and crucible. Impurities at the parts per million (ppm) level are readily determined with this system. For studies in high temperature chemistry, the crucible is replaced by a Knudsen cell[10], allowing equilibrium to be established between solid and vapor.

b. Electron Bombardment

In recent years, techniques have been developed to vaporize refractory solids by electron bombardment. With its supporting end water-cooled, the sample serves as its own crucible, which avoids the undesirable side-reactions encountered in the direct heating method mentioned above. A system which uses the same bombarding electron beam to ionize the vaporized species, and draws out axially the ions formed, has been described by WOLFF[11] for the production of carbon ions from graphite rods. Fig. 2 shows in diagrammatic form the annular tungsten filament which heats, by electron bombardment, a graphite cathode to 2400°K. The cathode, in turn, emits electrons which vaporize the graphite sample and ionize the resulting gas phase. This system protects the graphite sample from contamination by the W filament, and has produced 40μA ion currents. Depending on where they are formed, the ions have initial energies that range over the full electron accelerating potential. Therefore, a double-focusing instrument is required for mass analysis. As far as is known, this system has not yet been used in conjunction with a mass spectrograph.

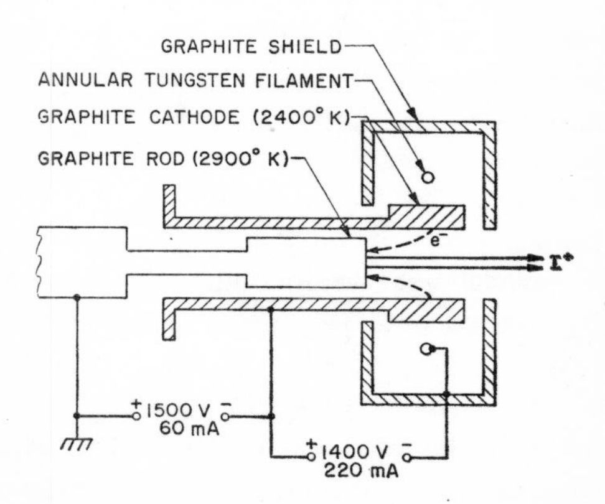

Fig. 2. Diagram of electron bombardment source.

References p. 53

c. Focused Radiation

The heating of solids to temperatures near 4000°K by focused radiation from an arc-image furnace is a well-established technique which recently has been applied to mass spectrometric problems. To go beyond 4000°K by other means is of special interest not only for high-temperature chemistry studies, but also for the production of thermal ions from those elements whose ionization potentials are too high for ordinary thermal ionization.

(i) Arc-image furnace

The design of an arc-image furnace for use with a 60° mass spectrometer was discussed by GOLDFINGER[12] several years ago. Recently, BURNS and collaborators[13] have reported on the vaporization of Al_2O_3 and of graphite, utilizing an arc-image furnace to heat the samples to temperatures of about 2500°K. The upper temperature limit attainable by this method appears to be about 3600°K.

(ii) Exploding-wire technique

While the exploding-wire technique is well-known, and its application to mass spectrometry was suggested many years ago[14], it is only recently that an effort has been made to use this method in high-temperature studies. LEIGH[15] has described work in which a metallic plasma is produced from refractory materials by means of an exploding wire, and the resulting ions analyzed in a time-of-flight mass spectrometer.

(iii) Laser source

The nearly parallel light beam obtainable from pulsed lasers can be readily focused onto very small areas, yielding very high radiation densities and producing extremely high surface temperatures. In this fashion, well-defined microvolumes, ranging from 20 to 100 μ in diameter and up to 1000 μ deep, have been vaporized from metals, semiconductors, and even sintered insulators[16,17] with an energy input of about 1 J. Concurrent with the vaporization of neutral particles, there are observed large pulses of thermal electrons (up to 10 A, 100 μsec long) and of thermal ions (about 100 mA, 100 μsec long). These pulses are found to be made up of individual spikes, 0.1 to 1 μsec long, which coalesce into a single pulse if the energy density is sufficiently great. The energy distribution of the emitted electrons indicates surface temperatures of about 10,000°K for metals, and 6000°K for semiconductors.

Fig. 3 shows in diagrammatic form how a laser source was incorporated[16] into a double-focusing mass spectrograph (Associated Electrical Industries Ltd. Type "MS7"). The nearly parallel laser beam entering through window W is focused internally by lens L onto target T. To optimize focusing and target location in the source, both L and T can be positioned independently with vacuum manipulators. The shield SH prevents the ions formed from being drained off to the vacuum housing which is at ground potential. Preliminary focusing adjustments are made with the help of a light beam on ground glass backing plate G, while target T is removed. After each laser pulse, the target can be moved sideways (normal to the paper plane) if a

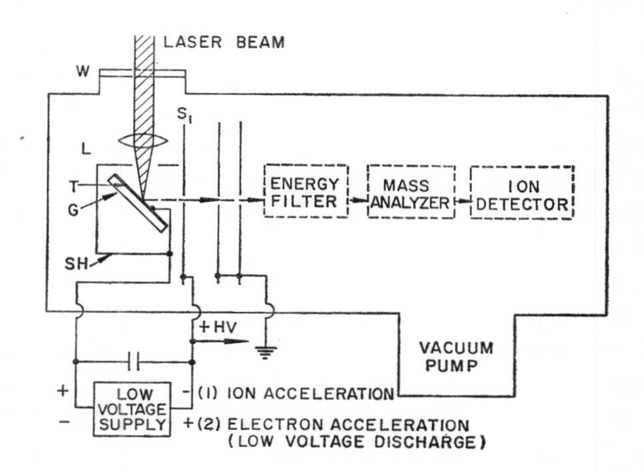

Fig. 3. Geometry and schematic diagram for laser ion source. (1) ion acceleration; (2) electron acceleration (low voltage discharge).

References p. 53

fresh surface is desired. The positive ions produced are accelerated into the double-focusing mass spectrograph, selected according to energy, mass-analyzed, and recorded on a photographic plate, which is the ideal detector for a short, single pulse. Each material is investigated in two ways:

(*a*) With an ion-accelerating potential applied between T and S_1, particles emitted from the target as *thermal ions* are detected. Only singly-charged thermal ions are found, while multiply-charged species are not detected. For different elements, relative intensities depend on the work function of the surface and on the ionization potential of the species in question, as predicted by the LANGMUIR–SAHA formula. So far, the photographic plate has recorded up to 10^8 thermal ions produced from a single laser pulse.

(*b*) With an electron-accelerating potential applied between T and S_1, a low-voltage arc discharge of the type to be discussed below is produced in the source, yielding large ion currents by electron impact ionization of *vaporized neutrals*. The ion spectra obtained in this fashion include considerable concentrations of singly- and multiply-charged species typical of the target, as well as species representing background gases. The considerable energy spread of these ions (about 100 eV) requires the use of a double-focusing machine. This discharge method produces up to 10^{10} ions per laser pulse from the vaporized neutrals, at a maximum ion current of about 10^{-5} A. For currents of such magnitude, space-charge effects become serious in the focused regions, in particular on the photographic plate. Inspection of these spectra shows indeed severe space-charge broadening of the major lines, whereas the weaker lines are not affected. To make quantitative measurements, it therefore is necessary to integrate over the line area. With the ion beam intensities obtained to date, it is possible to detect impurities down to a level of several parts per million.

Recently, a study has been published[18] in which the neutral vapor ejected by a focused laser beam from several solids was ionized by electron impact, mass analyzed, and detected with an electron multiplier. By indirect means, a temperature of about 4000°K was deduced which is characteristic of the expanded vapor cloud but is clearly much lower than the initial surface temperature.

d. Ion Bombardment

If surfaces rather than bulk material are to be studied, the production of ions by ion bombardment (sputtering) is indicated. This method requires complex equipment, but has the advantage that the sample can be kept at room temperature, a desirable feature in many investigations.

The geometry of a simple ion bombardment source[19] is shown in Fig. 4. Rare gas ions are produced by electron impact in box B_0, are accelerated and decelerated in lens system 1–2–3, and focused onto target T (typical current densities: 10^{-5} A/cm^2, for energies between 50 and 600 eV). The secondary neutrals emitted are ionized by electron beam I^-, while secondary ions enter directly the source region (S_1, S_2) and are subsequently mass-analyzed in

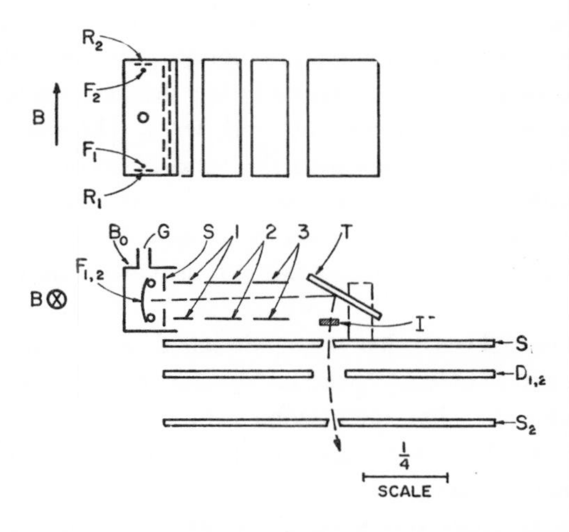

Fig. 4. Geometry of a simple ion bombardment source. B_0, box; $F_{1,2}$, filaments; S, slit plate; $R_{1,2}$, repellers; 1, 2 and 3, pairs of extraction electrodes; T, target; G, gas inlet; S_1, plate of first slit (0.010 in. × 0.5 in.); $D_{1,2}$, deflector half plates; S_2, plate of second slit (0.005 in. × 0.5 in.); I^-, ionizing electron beam; B, magnetic field intensity.

References p. 53

a single-focusing instrument. Many metals and semiconductors, elements as well as compounds, have been investigated with this geometry and with similar sources[19,20,21]. Recent advances made by LIEBL AND HERZOG[22], CASTAING AND SLODZIAN[23], and SMITH and co-workers[24] will be discussed below.

(i) Secondary ions

Qualitatively, the emission of secondary ions, positive as well as negative, can be predicted from the two forms of the LANGMUIR–SAHA formula (eqs. (1) and (2)). Positive ions are obtained from all elements with ionization potentials below about 10 eV, while negative ions are found for elements with electron affinities larger than 1 eV. The secondary ions have energy distributions between 2 and 30 eV.

LIEBL AND HERZOG[22] have described an improved sputtering source that utilizes a 1-mA primary ion beam of about 10 keV. Since this represents a power input of 10 W, the target has to be water-cooled to avoid thermal vaporization. The primary ion source and the target region are pumped by separate vacuum systems, so that the target remains at low pressure while it is being bombarded by the high-intensity ion beam. The high energy of the primary ion beam increases the yield of secondary ions and helps to reduce selectivity. The secondary ions are mass-analyzed in a small double-focusing machine of special design. A variety of samples, ranging from metals to insulators, have been investigated.

A "microanalyzer" has been designed and constructed by CASTAING AND SLODZIAN[23] who combine a sputtering source, mass spectrometer, and ion microscope into a single instrument, as follows: a small surface region of a solid sample is bombarded with a primary beam ($\sim 10^{-5}$ A) of rare gas ions of 10 keV energy. The secondary ions produced are mass-analyzed in a magnetic field and refocused onto an exit slit. The mass-separated ion bundle is post-accelerated and falls onto an image converter which produces tertiary electrons. These are accelerated in the opposite direction and fall on a fluorescent screen. Thus the screen images the spatial distribution of a given component existing at a given moment at the sample surface, over an area of about 10^{-2} cm^2. The magnification of the system is about 300, and the sensitivity depends strongly on the ionization potential of the atom in question. It is particularly promising for those samples that cannot be analyzed by the "electron microprobe". Because elemental sensitivities differ widely, the analyzer can be used for quantitative work only if it is calibrated with known samples.

(ii) Secondary neutrals

The selectivity encountered with secondary ions can be avoided by using secondary neutrals. However, since the pressure of background gases present in the sputtering source exceeds greatly that of the neutral beam, a pulsed primary ion beam together with a synchronous detection system should be used to reduce the background gas signal sufficiently. Such a system has been successfully employed by SMITH and co-workers[24] who use a relatively weak primary ion beam (about 10^{-6} A, energy up to 5 keV), a single-focusing mass spectrometer, and an electron multiplier. The sputtered neutrals, ionized by electron impact, yield currents of about 10^{-15} A.

e. *Vacuum Discharges*

There are several methods of ion production that are based on vacuum breakdown in a gap between two electrodes: the r.f. spark, the vibrating arc, and the pulsed d.c. arc. Two of these systems were already investigated by DEMPSTER[1] who, on the basis of equipment and circuitry available at that time, decided that the r.f. spark suited his purpose better. This Section will first define the basic terms used in vacuum breakdown and list the major parameters, then discuss the breakdown mechanism and, lastly, describe in detail the three types of vacuum discharge sources.

(i) Vacuum breakdown

First, it is desirable to define briefly the terms used, particularly

References p. 53

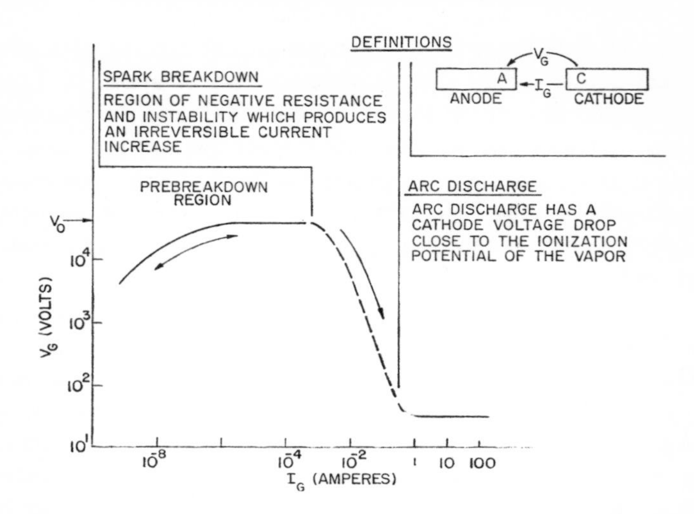

Fig. 5. Definitions and diagram for vacuum breakdown.

since in the past the words "spark" and "arc" have been employed loosely and interchangeably. Fig. 5 shows qualitatively the three major regions of vacuum breakdown on a voltage–current plot. As the potential applied between anode and cathode is gradually raised, *prebreakdown currents* appear whose values range up to a milliampere. In this prebreakdown region, the process is fully reversible. A further increase in potential produces catastrophic results, namely the *spark breakdown*, which is a region of negative resistance and instability and produces an *irreversible* current increase. In this region, the interelectrode potential drops sharply by about three orders of magnitude. If the external circuit has a sufficiently low impedance and enough energy has been stored, the spark breakdown leads to the *arc discharge* region which is characterized by currents of 10 to 100 or more amperes and a potential drop, occurring near the cathode, of between about 15 and 100 V.

The more important parameters to be considered for a detailed discussion of vacuum breakdown are summarized in Fig. 6. To have breakdown across a typical "narrow" gap ($d < 0.1$ cm), a voltage of 10^4 V or more is applied, which corresponds to an *average* field E_{AVE} near 10^6 V/cm. Since field emission of electrons, which is now known to initiate breakdown (see below), requires much larger fields, the *effective* field at the cathode, E_c, must be several orders of magnitude higher, presumably due to whisker growth. It is important to identify the charge carriers making up the gap current, and to determine their relative concentrations, in order to understand the breakdown details. While residual gases do not seem to play an important role once their pressure is below 10^{-6} torr, gases adsorbed on the surface and in the interior of the electrodes do influence the breakdown voltage. Other parameters to be investigated are the mechanical strength of the electrode material in strong electric fields, its vapor pressure, and the growth of microstructures or "whiskers".

Since 1950, an enormous volume of work has been published in an effort to understand the breakdown mechanism, yet until recently there were a number of conflicting hypotheses that beclouded the issue. Only the most significant recent studies can be briefly mentioned. CRANBERG, in his "clump hypothesis"[25], postulated that electrical stress, if sufficiently great, could remove

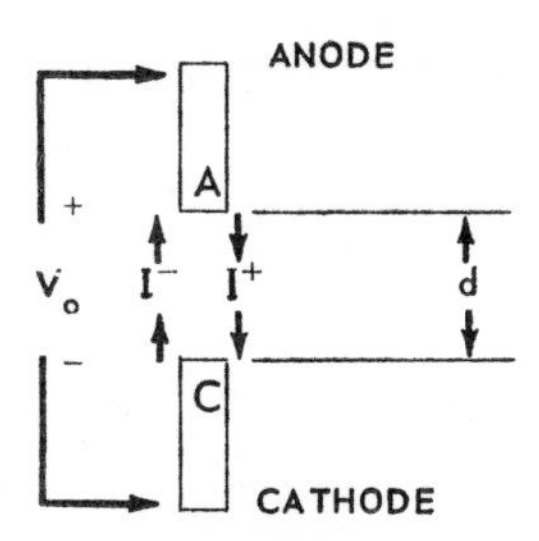

Fig. 6. Parameters essential for vacuum breakdown.
Summary: applied voltage, $V_0 = 10^4$–10^5V; gap, narrow, $d < 0.1$ cm, wide, $d > 0.1$ cm; average field, $E_{AVE} = V_0/d = 10^5$V cm^{-1}; effective fields, E_c, E_a; gap current, $I_g = I^+ + I^-$; residual pressure, $p = 10^{-6}$–10^{-9} torr. Electrode characteristics: bulk temperature T °K; gas content: bulk, surface; mechanical strength; vapor pressure; microstructure (whiskers).

References p. 53

charged microscopic aggregates or clumps from either electrode. These clumps are then accelerated across the gap and produce heating and vaporization of the opposite electrode. To date, no experimental proof has been presented that this mechanism initiates breakdown, although it is possible that it plays a role at a later stage. On the other hand, the field emission theory proposed by BOYLE, KISLIUK AND GERMER[26] is borne out by many different experiments, including those by PIVOVAR AND GORDIENKO[27], GOLDMAN AND GOLDMAN[28], DEGEETER[29], LITTLE AND WHITNEY[30], ALPERT and collaborators[31], and BRODIE[32].

The initial step of electron emission from the cathode may lead to partial vaporization of the emitting whisker, and this is followed by heating of the anode, as established by several material-transfer studies. TARASOVA AND RAZIN[33] used irradiated Cu electrodes to show that, during prebreakdown, there is material transfer mainly from anode to cathode. Similar results were obtained by SCHWABE[34] who used two dissimilar electrodes and determined by emission spectrography the preferred direction of transfer. Recently, this author and coworkers[35] have used mass spectrometry to show that in d.c. arc pulses of one μsec duration the vapor consists largely of anode material.

From the information presented above, one can postulate the following sequence of events occurring during the breakdown of a narrow gap, which is shown in diagrammatic form in Fig. 7.

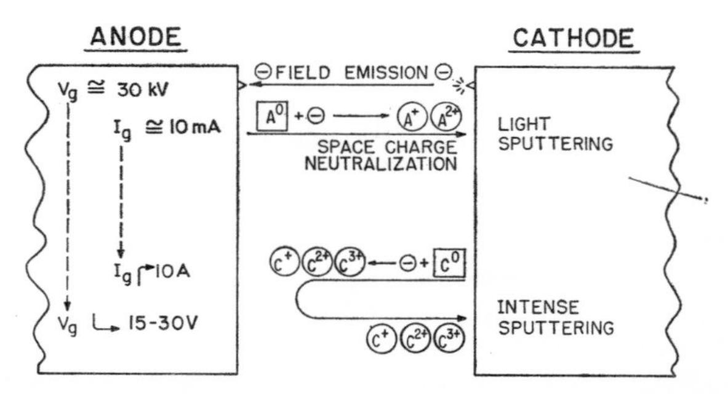

Fig. 7. Steps leading to high voltage breakdown of a narrow gap.

As the average field between electrodes is raised to about 10^6 V/cm, a small predischarge current begins to flow which is due to field emission from one or more whiskers on the cathode surface. If the current density is sufficiently high, the whisker will melt and partially vaporize, thereby contributing some cathode atoms to the vapor phase. Electron bombardment of the anode vaporizes anode atoms which probably come from anode whiskers, as well as O^+ ions from adsorbed CO. The neutral atoms from anode and cathode are ionized by cathode electrons and help increase the electron current intensity by space charge neutralization. Furthermore, the ions bombard the cathode, producing mainly sputtered neutrals and some secondary electrons. As the electron and ion currents build up in intensity, the interelectrode potential drops, as shown qualitatively in Fig. 5. During this spark breakdown stage, the production of singly-charged ions predominates, but multiply-charged species are also found. If there is enough energy stored in the external circuit, the current build-up continues through heavy sputtering, ending in the arc discharge defined above. In this mode, gap voltages of between 15 and 30 V are measured, and high concentrations of multiply-charged ions are observed, which is typical of plasma conditions.

At first sight, it seems contradictory that multiply-charged ions requiring ionizing energies up to 100 eV or more should appear in considerable concentrations at a stage when the gap voltage has dropped to 15–30 V. However, it will be shown below that ion energy distributions measured for arc discharges indicate plasma potentials up to 100 V, and, furthermore, theory predicts that in a plasma multiply-charged ions are produced by multiple-collision processes.

(ii) The r.f. spark

Although the r.f. spark is, to date, the most widely used vacuum discharge method, relatively few studies have been made to investigate its basic properties. FRANZEN[36] obtained oscillograms of the gap voltage which show that the r.f. spark consists of a sequence of individual breakdowns, occurring only during selected

References p. 53

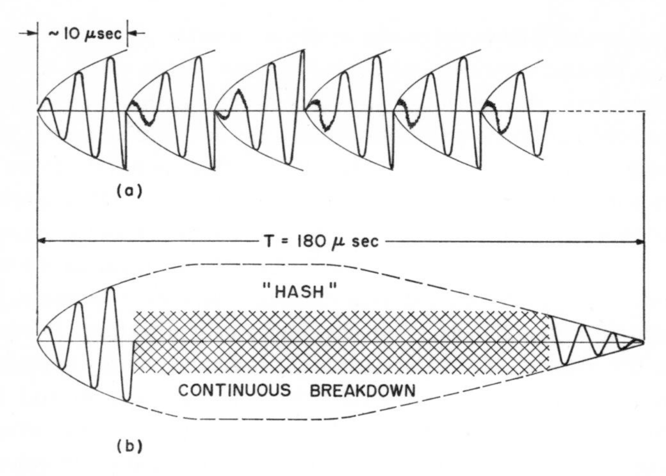

Fig. 8. Comparison of breakdown patterns for the r.f. spark. (a) From J. FRANZEN, *Z. Naturforsch.*, 18a (1963) 410; (b) RCA (MS7).

half-cycles (see Fig. 8a). The r.f. voltage ($f = 1$ Mc/sec) builds up during a period of about 10 μsec to a point where breakdown occurs, as indicated by the heavy, wiggly trace which persists for about two half-cycles. When the energy stored in the Tesla coil circuit[37] has been exhausted, the breakdown terminates, but in the meantime the r.f. voltage is building up again, and the process may be repeated several times if the pulse is long enough. Fig. 8b shows a different pattern, observed for the MS7 used at RCA Laboratories. After an initial build-up at the beginning of the pulse, continuous breakdown occurs which appears as "hash" and which terminates a few cycles before the end of the pulse. It is presumed that the breakdown is continuous because the coil circuit (typical impedance: ~ 20,000 Ω) is capable of storing sufficient energy. HICKAM AND SWEENEY[38] have presented evidence that in their instrument breakdown can occur once every half-cycle during most of the pulse.

FRANZEN[36] has presented a model for the acceleration of ions in the increasing r.f. field which permits an estimate of their initial energy in terms of time and place of origin. Actual measurements

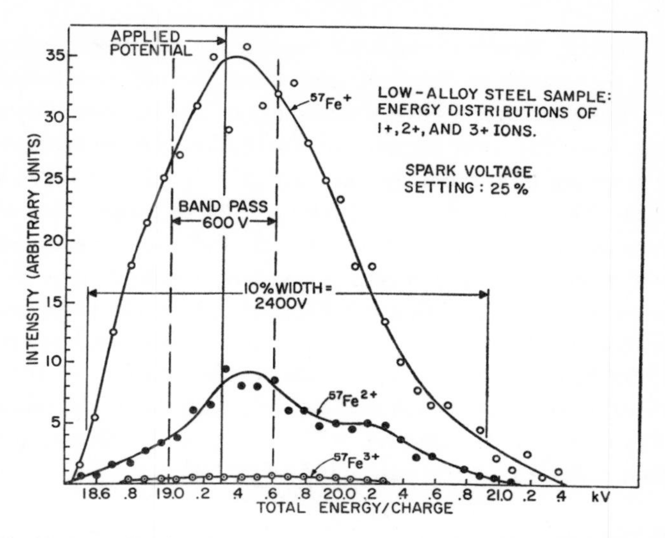

Fig. 9. Energy distributions for Fe ions produced in the r.f. spark from a low-alloy steel sample.

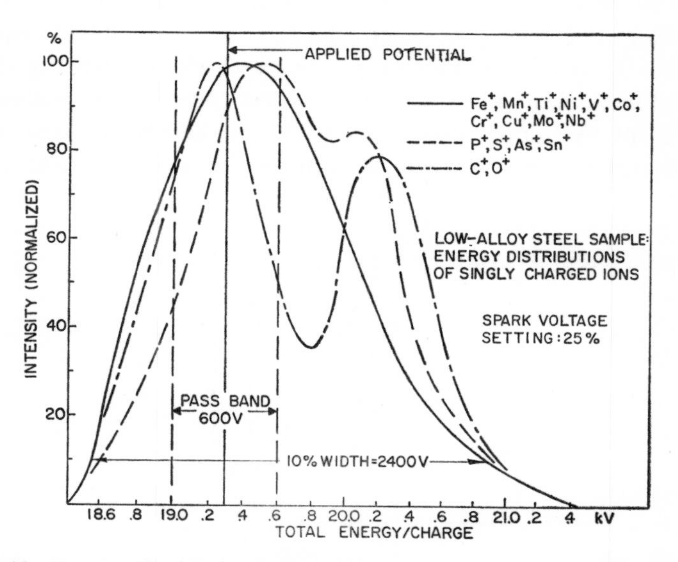

Fig. 10. Energy distribution for low-alloy steel matrix and impurity ions produced in the r.f. spark.

References p. 53

of ion energy distributions have been made by WOOLSTON AND HONIG for total ion beams[39] and mass-resolved ion beams[40]. Fig. 9 presents typical energy distributions for various iron ions from a low-alloy steel sample. In this figure, the dependence of plate response on ion energy (see Section 3.d) was not taken into account. The distributions are about 2400 eV wide, and their maxima lie close to the applied potential and close to each other. Fig. 10 summarizes the results for various impurity ions in the same matrix and shows that most species, except the very volatile ones, have similar distributions. This explains why analyses made with the MS7 are not seriously affected by changes in the ion accelerating potential, which is at variance with the results reported by FRANZEN AND HINTENBERGER[37], who used a different source geometry and an energy pass band of 200 eV.

(iii) The vibrating arc

This ion source, already described by DEMPSTER[1], has enjoyed a sudden revival within the last two years[41–48]. In most of these studies, a very simple electro-mechanical low-voltage system, similar to that of a doorbell circuit, is employed (see Fig. 11). The functioning of the vibrating arc has recently been discussed in detail by SCHUY AND FRANZEN[49] who investigated the time dependence of gap current and voltage, as well as ion and light

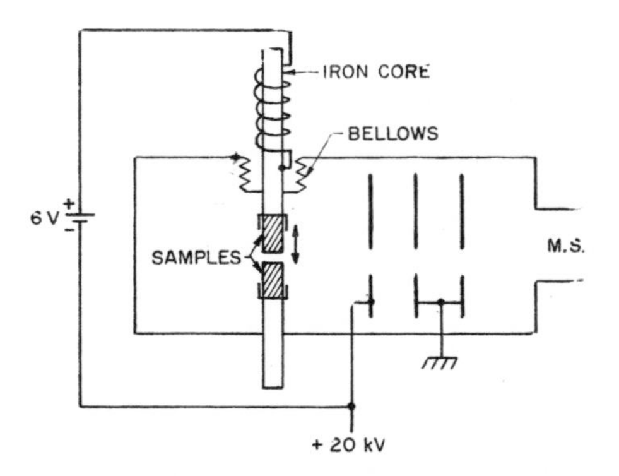

Fig. 11. Schematic of simple vibrating arc circuit.

emission with the help of a dual-trace oscilloscope. While the interelectrode gap is open, the gap voltage is the applied voltage of about 6 V. When the gap closes, the voltage drops to zero, while the current increases exponentially which, in turn, gradually reduces the contact pressure to zero. At this point, the contact resistance becomes very large, produces melting of the contact areas, and results in a "liquid bridge" as the electrodes move apart. When the liquid bridge breaks, an arc keeps the current of about 15 A flowing, at a gap voltage of about 20 V. Ion and light emission are observed only during this arcing period. Sometimes, the liquid bridge is reformed, and the arcing process may be repeated. When the arc finally goes out, an inductive voltage kick is observed.

The vibrating arc works well with conducting electrodes, but not at all with high-resistivity semiconductors. It is not applicable to materials of insufficient mechanical strength, such as compressed powders or brittle materials and it is not possible to make very short exposures with this system. Among the ions produced, the doubly-charged species predominate over singly- and triply-charged ions, the distribution being typical of an arc discharge. When dissimilar electrodes are employed, the spectrum shows mostly cathode ions.

(iv) The pulsed d.c. arc

Recently, work has been done at RCA Laboratories[35] to utilize pulsed d.c. voltages for vacuum breakdown and produce intense ion beams with moderate energy distributions. This Section will first deal with the short "trigger" pulse, discuss the circuitry developed and results obtained, then describe the longer low-voltage discharge.

a) Short trigger. The most convenient means of producing a trigger pulse of a few μsec duration between two sample electrodes is a pulse transformer since it isolates the associated circuitry from the high potential (+ 20 kV) of the mass spectrograph source. Fig. 12 is a block diagram of the system used. It delivers, at

References p. 53

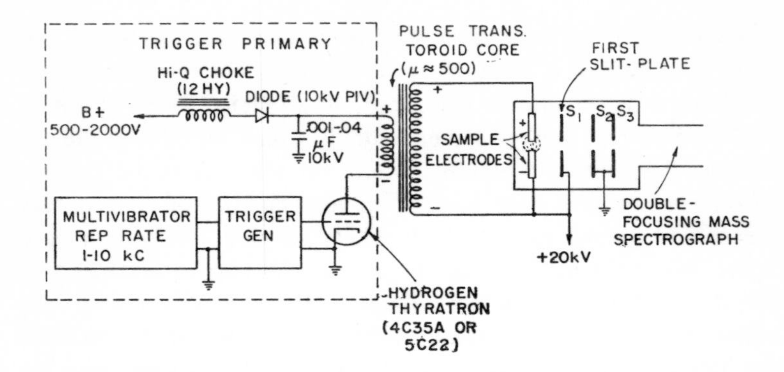

Fig. 12. Diagram of short trigger circuit.

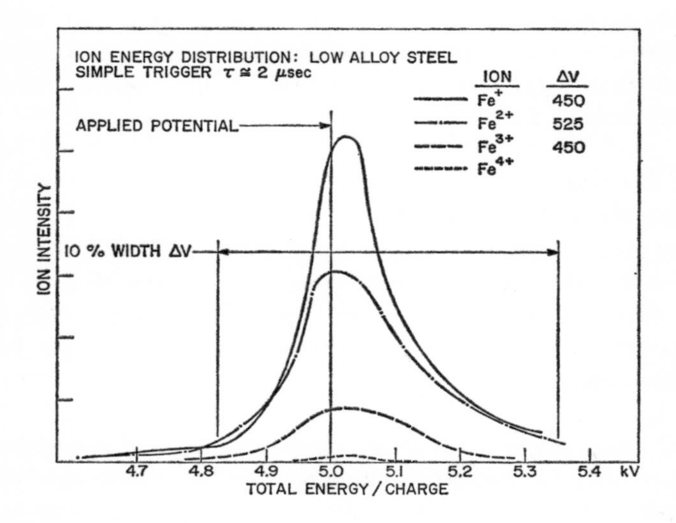

Fig. 13. Energy distributions for Fe ions produced in a short trigger discharge from a low-alloy steel sample.

repetition rates up to 3000 c/sec, a high-voltage pulse of up to 60 kV which causes breakdown of the vacuum gap and results in a current pulse of from 5 to 50 A, between 1 and 4 μsec wide, depending on the transformer design and the value of the capacitor in the trigger primary circuit. Positive ion pulses (up to 10 mA) produced in the expanding discharge reach the first slit plate S_1 where a small fraction enters the mass spectrograph to be energy-selected and mass-analyzed. Fig. 13 presents some mass-analyzed energy distribution plots obtained for the various iron ions from a low-alloy steel. The relative ion intensities (corrected for dependence of plate response on ion energy) indicate that Fe^+, Fe^{2+}, and Fe^{3+} are the three important species, and that their ΔV is about 500 eV.

(b) Triggered low-voltage discharge. Fig. 14 is a block diagram of the first and simplest variant of various triggered low-voltage systems tried to date. It consists of an adjustable low-voltage supply connected in series with the pulse transformer secondary. In its simplest form, the low-voltage supply is a 90 V battery in parallel with a set of capacitors ranging from 2 to 40 μF. It yields a gap current pulse that decreases exponentially and is adjustable in width from about 10 to 200 μsec. If a true square pulse is desired, the simple low-voltage supply is replaced by a pulser of suitable design. The diode shown in Fig. 14 shorts out the high impedance of the pulse transformer secondary during the low-

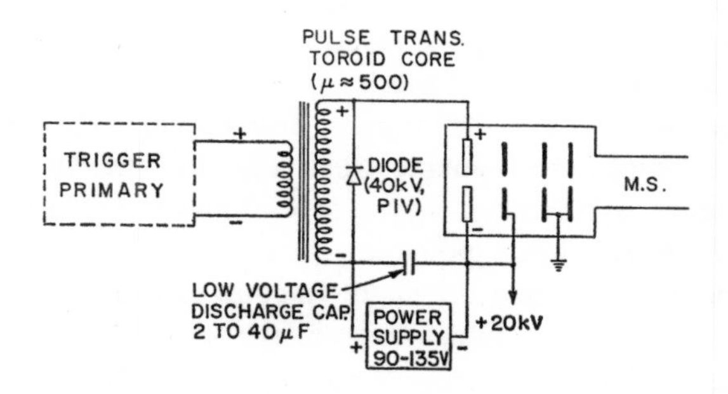

Fig. 14. Diagram of triggered low-voltage circuit.

References p. 53

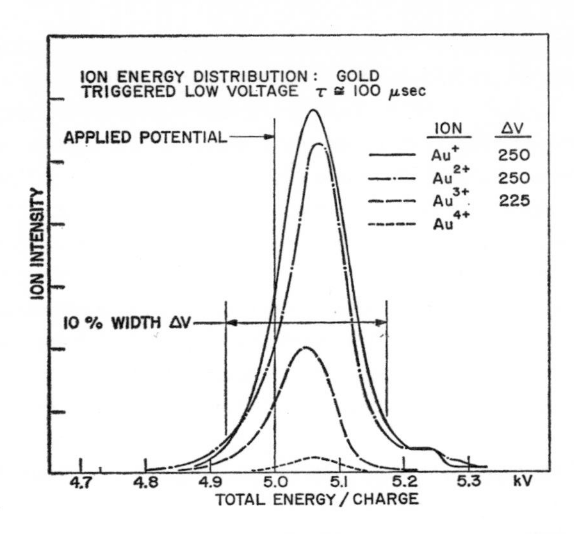

Fig. 15. Energy distributions for Au ions produced in a triggered low-voltage discharge.

voltage pulse, allowing the low-voltage supply to furnish the gap current necessary to sustain the discharge. A portion of the positive ions formed in the discharge arrive at S_1 and pass into the mass spectrograph.

The energy distribution of the ions produced from gold electrodes in the low-voltage discharge (Fig. 15) is about 250 eV wide and has its maximum about 60 eV above the applied potential. Ion intensities, corrected for plate response, show that the intensity of doubly- and triply-charged species has increased significantly, as compared with the short trigger distribution. The measured width ΔV, while much smaller than that for the short trigger, still exceeds considerably the voltage supplied (90 V) and the measured interelectrode potential drop (about 30 V). There is substantial evidence that the major fraction of the apparent width of 250 V is due to a voltage drop in the 20 kV ion accelerating supply under pulsed load conditions. Davis and Miller[50] recently studied the charge and energy distributions of ions formed in a drawn arc of 0.1 sec duration, and found 10% widths of about 75 V, while the distribution maxima lay about 60 V above cathode potential. It has been suggested[51] that these 60 V displacements can be explained by the fact that the potential of the thermal plasma produced lies about 60 V above cathode level.

(v) Performance comparison

To compare the performance of the three vacuum discharge methods and, at the same time, arrive at a better understanding of the basic processes involved, a number of tests have been carried out recently at RCA Laboratories which will be described below.

(a) Charge distribution. In an extended series of runs, the distribution among singly- and multiply-charged species was studied for the compound $SnNb_3$, employing the three vacuum discharge methods. Single pulses were used in all cases except for the r.f. spark where this was not possible. It was found that relative intensities of the various species changed widely from pulse to pulse, but that the average values shown in Table II correlate reasonably well with gap currents. The intensity values (corrected

TABLE II

CHARGE DISTRIBUTION FOR IONS FROM $SnNb_3$

System	Pulse length τ (μsec)	Gap current I_G (A)	Sn			Nb		
			+	2+	3+	+	2+	3+
r.f. spark	25–200	~ 0.1	1.0	0.3	0.05	1.0	0.3	0.05
Simple trigger	~ 1	4	1.0	0.4		1.0	0.4	0.07
	~ 4	30	1.0	1.5	0.5	1.0	1.5	0.7
Triggered l.v. discharge	20–100	30	1.0	1.5	0.3	1.0	1.5	0.6
Vibrating arc	20	30	1.0	1.3	0.5	1.0	1.4	0.7

References p. 53

for plate response) shown in Table II confirm the well-known fact that in the r.f. spark the singly-charged species predominate, and it is interesting to note that this is also true for the shortest trigger pulse obtainable (1 μsec). For the r.f. spark, only singly-, doubly-, and triply-charged species have been shown, even though ions carrying up to fourteen charges were observed on long exposures for some of the elements.

When the simple trigger pulse is lengthened to 4 μsec, the ion spectrum changes to the distribution typical of the arc discharge, with the doubly-charged species becoming predominant. It is seen that the distribution is about the same for the 4 μsec-long simple trigger, the triggered low-voltage discharge, and the vibrating arc, all of which have approximately the same gap current of 30 A. It should be noted that in the arc discharge the X^{4+} intensities fall off very rapidly and that the more highly ionized species are barely visible. This charge distribution is qualitatively compatible with the thermal plasma potential of 60 V mentioned above. FRANZEN and collaborators[52] have attempted to explain quantitatively the charge distribution observed in a vibrating arc discharge in terms of plasma temperature and electron pressure, using the SAHA equation. Assuming a neutral plasma that is in thermal equilibrium and a temperature distribution that depends on time and space, they computed charge distributions that parallel closely their values observed for a number of impurities.

Since the different low-voltage systems produce doubly- and triply-charged species in large concentrations (lines 3, 4, and 5, Table II), these species as well as singly-charged ions must be taken into account for analytical applications. If their intensity ratios are constant, any single major species can be used, if not, it is necessary to add up intensities. In their recent study, FRANZEN and collaborators[52] have investigated the charge distribution in a triggered d.c. arc. With the help of a time-gating circuit, they observed that in the early discharge stage the distribution resembles that of the r.f. spark, while the later stages show the typical arc distribution, in agreement with the results presented in Tables II and III (see below).

TABLE III

DISSIMILAR ELECTRODE STUDIES

Anode: Ni; Cathode: Cu

System	Pulse length τ (μsec)	Series resistance R_S (Ω)	Gap current I_G (A)	Ratios		
				Ni^+/Cu^+	Ni^{2+}/Ni^+	Cu^{2+}/Cu^+
Simple trigger	~ 4	20,000	0.1 (est.)	6	0.1	
		0	30	0.2		0.4
Triggered l.v. discharge	20–100	200	4	0.3	0.4	0.8
		0	30	0.2	0.9	1.1

(b) Dissimilar electrode studies. In order to study the material transport between electrodes and to support the breakdown hypothesis presented above, tests were made using two dissimilar electrodes. In earlier work[35], Au–Pt electrode pairs had been used, while in the present study a Ni–Cu pair was employed. By placing a series resistance of appropriate value in the electrode circuit, it was possible to limit the discharge to its early stage (Table III, top line). The ions observed represented mostly *anode* material and had a charge distribution similar to that of the r.f. spark. With the series resistance removed (Table III, second line), *cathode* ions exceed anode ions by a factor of five to one, which agrees qualitatively with observations reported earlier[35]. Attempts to change similarly the gap current in a triggered low-voltage discharge with a series resistance were partially successful, showing a slight, though significant increase of cathode ions with gap current (lines 3 and 4, Table III).

(c) Performance comparison. Table IV summarizes the performance of the pulsed d.c. arc sources and compares it to that of the r.f. source. The vibrating arc characteristics are very similar to those shown in the third column for the triggered low-voltage

References p. 53

TABLE IV

COMPARISON OF SOURCE PERFORMANCE: TRIGGERED LOW-VOLTAGE *vs.* R.F.

Parameter	Triggered low voltage		r. f.
	Trigger	t.l.v.	
Monitor current			
Stability	acceptable	acceptable	poor
Max. value, ave.	10^{-9}	10^{-8}	10^{-9}
Max. value, pulse	10^{-8}	10^{-7}	10^{-8}
Minimum time for 10^{-6} C exposure (min)	60	6	30
Shortest exposure (C)	$< 10^{-14}$	10^{-12}	$3 \cdot 10^{-14}$
Shortest exposure (ions)	$< 6 \cdot 10^{4}$	$6 \cdot 10^{6}$	$2 \cdot 10^{5}$
En. distr.: 10% width (kV)	0.6	0.2	1 – 2.5
Usable fraction of en. band	1	1	0.2 – 0.5
Ratio atoms/ion	10^{7}	10^{7}	$5 \cdot 10^{7}$
Gap current (A)	10	10	(0.1)

system. It is of interest to note that the ion currents produced in the low-voltage sources are more stable than those from the r.f. source, and that the sample position needs to be readjusted less frequently, which is of considerable practical value. For analytical applications, it is important that exposures can be made short enough to produce barely visible lines from the matrix material. Table IV shows that the short trigger readily fulfills this requirement. Energy distributions have been compared in terms of the "10% width", *i.e.* the separation, in eV, of the two points where the intensity has dropped off to 10% of its maximum value. Since the MS7 monitor system accepts an energy band of 600 eV, essentially all the ions formed in the pulsed d.c. arc sources can be utilized. In contrast, the ions formed in the r.f. source have much larger energy distributions (1–2.5 kV), which limits the fraction of ions that can be used.

An estimate of the overall efficiency of a given ion source used in conjunction with the mass spectrograph is obtained from the ratio of sample atoms vaporized per ion arriving at the photographic plate. This is readily computed from weight measurements made on the sample rods before and after a given exposure recorded by the integrator. The integrated monitor current yields the total number of ions arriving at the plate, provided monitor current and plate current are equal. The ratios of atoms vaporized per ion recorded (the inverse of the "overall yield" to be discussed in Section 3) for the low-voltage sources indicate a sample consumption that is considerably lower than that of the r.f. source.

3. ION YIELDS, SENSITIVITIES, AND ERRORS

(i) Definitions

For the purpose of this discussion, the *overall yield* $Y_o(x)$ of component x is defined as the number of ions detected per sample atom vaporized:

$$Y_o(x) = I_d(x)/A(x) = Y_s(x) \cdot f(t) \cdot f(d) \tag{3}$$

where

$I_d(x)$ = number of ions arriving at detector
$A(x)$ = number of sample atoms vaporized
$Y_s(x) = I_s(x)/A(x)$ = *source yield*
$I_s(x)$ = number of ions produced in source
$f(t)$ = instrumental transmission factor
$f(d)$ = detector response factor.

For a typical double-focusing mass spectrograph, the value of $Y_o(x)$ lies between 10^{-7} and 10^{-8}.

If quantitative analyses are to be made, the most important parameter is the *relative sensitivity coefficient* for component x:

$$S_R(x) = Y_o(x)/Y_o(m) \tag{4}$$

where m represents the matrix material. In a given matrix, relative sensitivities for all constituents are determined empirically by analyzing calibration samples which contain impurities in known concentrations. The following Sections will first discuss separately

References p. 53

source yield, transmission factor, and detector response, and then deal with relative sensitivity coefficients and errors.

(ii) Source yields

The number of ions produced at a given time from a given component present in the sample depends on many factors. These include:

(a) for the solid sample: local impurity concentrations, local and bulk temperatures, thermal conductivity, diffusion coefficient, work function, heat of vaporization, and sputtering yield;

(b) for vaporized particles: kinetic energy, ionization potential and cross section, partial pressure, and condensation coefficient;

(c) for ionizing electrons: energy and density.

The relative importance of these factors depends on the method of ion production employed. For the simplest case, that of thermal ionization, source yields can be predicted directly from the LANGMUIR–SAHA formula (eq. (1)). Ion densities produced from neutral vapor by electron impact can be evaluated from a knowledge of sample temperature, source geometry, ionization cross section, and electron energy and current[9], which leads to the following expression for the source yield

$$Y_s(x) = \frac{\dot{I}_s(x)}{\dot{A}(x)} = \frac{\sigma(x)I^- l}{3.63 \cdot 10^3 q^+ a} \left[\frac{M(x)}{T}\right]^{1/2} \tag{5}$$

where, for component x,

$\dot{I}_s(x)$ = rate of ion production, in sec^{-1}
$\dot{A}(x)$ = rate of vaporization of neutrals, in sec^{-1}
$\sigma(x)$ = ionization cross section, in cm^2
I^- = ionizing electron current, in A
l = ionizing path of electrons, in cm
q^+ = single charge carried by each ion $= 1.6 \cdot 10^{-19}$ C
T = absolute temperature of sample, in °K
$M(x)$ = atomic mass, in a.m.u.
a = area of neutral beam intersecting electron beam, in cm^2.

Substituting reasonable values into eq. (5), source yields between 10^{-4} and 10^{-5} are obtained.

On the other hand, ion formation by the discharge methods is far more complex and involves probably most of the factors listed above, which makes it difficult, if not impossible, to obtain an estimate of absolute source yields. However, based on energy utilization, it seems clear that the atomic heat of vaporization of the species in question must enter inversely, and the ionization cross section directly.

(iii) Instrumental transmission factor

Individual ion densities transmitted by the instrument are affected by a number of interdependent parameters, in particular energy and charge distributions of the species and the instrumental geometry. Since energy distributions can differ widely, especially for volatile components[40], this parameter deserves special consideration, particularly in instruments where the energy pass band is small compared to the total distribution. Among the geometrical factors, the electrode arrangement in the ion source will be considered first. There is experimental evidence to show that interelectrode gap width plays an important role. WOOLSTON AND HONIG[39] noticed that in the r.f. spark source the ion energy distribution widens significantly with increasing gap width or spark voltage. HALLIDAY, SWIFT AND WOLSTENHOLME[53] found that the concentration of volatile constituents increases when the spark voltage is raised. Similarly, FRANZEN *et al.*[52] reported that volatile constituents and multiply-charged species become more abundant with increasing gap width which they explain as follows: as the gap width is increased, the size of the anode spot grows which reduces the anode temperature and, thereby, the vaporization of low vapor pressure elements. At the same time, the ion transit time increases, which gives multiply-charged species a better chance to be formed. Since the sample electrodes change shape continuously during the spark or arc discharge, it is in practice difficult to keep the gap width constant during a run unless the breakdown voltage is monitored on an oscilloscope[54]. The location of the

References p. 53

sample electrodes within the ion source is also of considerable importance. GLASS[55] found that the relative concentration of multiply-charged ions depends in a sensitive fashion on the position of the electrodes with respect to the first slit plate and to the major instrumental axis. This effect is presumably caused by variations in the energy-dependent location of the ion focus near the source exit slit which affects the angular selection by the aperture slit and, thereby, the transmission efficiency in the instrument. In turn, variations in the angular selection may lead to an instability in the monitor to plate current ratio, which makes accurate analyses difficult.

To minimize effects due to mass discrimination, a plane-parallel ion source geometry[56] rather than a focusing ion lens system[37] should be employed. FRANZEN *et al.*[52] have recently described a plane-parallel source that uses wire grids instead of slits and produces parallel ion beams of uniform composition. However, this system presents some serious drawbacks: the material sputtered from the grids contributes to an impurity background, and the grids may become clogged by deposits from the samples.

Variations in line shape have to be taken into account in all double-focusing instruments that use photographic recording. For the MATTAUCH–HERZOG geometry, the theoretical line width is proportional[42] to $M^{1/2}$, but in practice several other contributing factors must be considered also: the location of the discharge between the electrodes, and of the sample within the ion source; space-charge broadening within the major ion beam and at the photoplate; charge-up effects caused by insulating layers in the source region or in the electrostatic analyzer; fluctuations of electric and magnetic fields; and unintentional displacement of plate from focal plane. The line length increases significantly with mass in instruments without z-axis focusing. In the case of the MS7, this increase amounts to about 30% between the low-mass and high-mass ends of the plate[57].

(iv) Detector response factor

If ion-sensitive plates are used to record ion densities, the plate response to be discussed in Chapter III must be considered. Since analyses are usually made at a fixed ion accelerating potential, the energy dependence does not come into play, except when multiply-charged ions are used (an ion of type X^{n+} carries an energy nqV, where V = accelerating potential). On the other hand, the correction for mass dependence must be applied on a routine basis.

If the detection system includes an electron multiplier, its response is best determined empirically and should be taken into account in analytical applications.

(v) Relative sensitivity coefficients

While there is now available a fair volume of data on relative sensitivities obtained in r.f. spark source instruments, a meaningful comparison is difficult to make because only in few instances has sufficient information been presented concerning the contributing factors discussed above. AHEARN[58] has summarized most of the data available for different matrices up to May 1963. In addition, a number of authors have published sensitivities of impurities in different matrices, as follows: A.E.I.[46,53,56,59] in Fe, Al, and several Cu calibration samples; OWENS AND GIARDINO[60] in NBS type 442 stainless steel; GOSHGARIAN AND JENSEN[61] in Hastalloy; AULINGER[62] in Fe; CHUPAKHIN AND GLAVIN[63] in Al; and KAWANO[64] in Cu, Zn, Mg, and Fe.

GOSHGARIAN AND JENSEN[61] have computed relative sensitivity coefficients which appear to be in good agreement with their measured values. These coefficients are based on atomic areas, ionization potentials, heats of vaporization, and atomic mass. Of these contributing factors, only the last two can be justified on theoretical grounds: for a given energy input, the number of atoms vaporized will depend inversely on their heat of vaporization, and the plate response is proportional to M^{-y}, with y ranging[60,65,66] between 0.5 and 0.8. On the other hand, it is unlikely that atomic areas derived from covalent radii represent adequately ionization cross sections, and there is no reason to assume that ionization potentials contribute in linear fashion to sensitivity.

This author[67] has used ionization cross sections computed by OTVOS AND STEVENSON[68], heats of vaporization, and atomic

References p. 53

masses to estimate relative sensitivity coefficients for many elements in the Atomic Table, using Fe as reference. While agreement between computed and measured values available in 1964 appeared satisfactory, the lack of consistency of the most recent experimental data[59] suggests that it may be premature to make such comparisons. However, it may be broadly stated that relative sensitivity coefficients of most elements differ by less than a factor of five.

ADDINK[69] correlates sensitivity coefficients with boiling point differences between matrix and impurity, and with diffusion constants. The boiling point differences are equivalent to the heat of vaporization factor, while diffusion effects should certainly be considered, especially at elevated electrode temperatures. However, it appears that these coefficients cannot be predicted, but were established with the help of known calibration samples.

(vi) Errors

If solids mass spectrography is to be used as a quantitative analytical tool, the most important practical question to be asked is: "With what fidelity do the ion currents registered by the detector represent the impurity concentrations existing in the sample?" While a partial answer to this question can be found dispersed throughout earlier portions of this Section, it appears worthwhile to review this problem in terms of potential errors connected with the sample, the ion source, the analyzer, and the detector. The discussion will be limited to a double-focusing mass spectrograph using photoplate detection.

(a) Sample inhomogeneity. Analytical errors caused by local variations of impurity concentrations in the sample have been considered in some detail by HALLIDAY and collaborators[53]. They computed for five matrices the sample volumes that will be consumed in the analysis of a given impurity x from the formula

$$V(\mathrm{m}) = \frac{10^6 \cdot I_{\mathrm{d}}(\mathrm{x,i}) \cdot M(\mathrm{m})}{N \cdot \delta(\mathrm{m}) \cdot F(\mathrm{i}) \cdot Y_{\mathrm{o}}(\mathrm{x}) \cdot C(\mathrm{x})} \tag{6}$$

where

$V(\mathrm{m})$ = matrix volume consumed, in cm^3
$I_\mathrm{d}(\mathrm{x,i})$ = measurable number of ions of isotope i of impurity x, arriving at detector (assumed to be 10^5)
$M(\mathrm{m})$ = molecular weight of matrix m, in a.m.u.
N = Avagadro's number = $6.02 \cdot 10^{23}$ particles per gram-molecular weight
$\delta(\mathrm{m})$ = density of matrix, in $\mathrm{g/cm}^3$
$F(\mathrm{i})$ = fractional abundance of isotope i used
$Y_\mathrm{o}(\mathrm{x})$ = overall yield, as defined in eq. (3)
$C(\mathrm{x})$ = concentration of impurity x, in ppm atomic.

It is seen that for higher impurity concentrations this volume decreases, leading to more stringent requirements of sample homogeneity. In typical cases, impurities at the 10 to 1000 ppm level are equivalent to volumes consumed whose linear dimensions range from 15 to 300 μ. If there are present in the sample any impurity inclusions of similar dimensions, it is obvious that repeat analyses can be subject to considerable standard deviations. When the sample volume consumed is very small, inhomogeneity effects can be reduced [52] by running the spark continuously, but allowing ions to arrive at the detector only intermittently, thereby increasing the sample volume consumed.

It is sometimes difficult to differentiate between inhomogeneously distributed bulk impurities and surface contaminants which may have been deposited by improper etching procedures. It would therefore seem worthwhile to study in more detail ways and means to reduce surface contamination by improved etching techniques.

(b) Ion source. It is obvious that operating conditions in the ion source will affect strongly the relative concentrations of ions produced. The single most important parameter to produce variations and errors is the temperature of the sample electrodes during operation. This temperature depends on the thermal conductivity of the sample and, for a given type of discharge, on voltage, pulse length, and repetition rate employed. As pointed out by ADDINK [69], different impurities will at elevated temperatures

References p. 53

diffuse to the surface at different rates, which, together with their partial pressures, will affect their measured concentrations. Variations of temperature with time will be reflected in the vaporization rates of each component which results in a lack of reproducibility from exposure to exposure. The partial pressures of background gases in the source affect not only the surface impurities found, but also, to some extent, the breakdown voltage and thereby the sample temperature. Therefore, sample and source region should be baked to obtain optimum results.

The ionization potential of a given impurity, in conjunction with the work function of the sample surface, determines the fraction of particles vaporized as ions, as discussed in Section 2a. Since thermal ionization contributes significantly to the production of singly-charged ions of Group IA, IIA, and some other elements, it is necessary in these cases to utilize the doubly-charged species for analytical purposes and to assume reasonable ratios of doubly- to singly-charged species.

Another parameter to be taken into account for a given impurity is its condensation coefficient on the sample and source surfaces, since this determines whether a particle can pass through the interelectrode gap more than once. In this respect, the pulsed d.c. arc and vibrating arc systems with their unidirectional particle flow (see Section 2.e.v) are preferable to the r.f. spark source where electrode material may be shuttled back and forth several times during successive half-cycles. In fact, the arc systems may be used to advantage in the exploration of surfaces with counterelectrodes, since under proper running conditions the ion contribution from the counterelectrode can be minimized.

(c) Analyzer. While the effects of sample and source geometry and of ion generating methods on charge and energy distribution and on line character have already been discussed above, the emphasis will now be placed on the resulting errors. All analyses depend directly on a knowledge of the distribution of ion current between monitor and photoplate. Even if the absolute value of this current ratio should not be known, analyses can be carried

out, provided the ratio remains constant from exposure to exposure and is independent of source conditions. Judging from a large number of analyses, this author concludes that large errors are apt to arise when very short exposures are used to determine the plate sensitivity from a matrix line, and that even normal exposures may be seriously off in an unpredictable manner. Zero drift and amplifer noise are presumably responsible for the difficulties encountered in measuring short exposures, while the case of the longer exposures is not so clear-cut. The latter problem may well be due to unexplained shifts in the position of the ion beam which could lead to variations in the current ratio. Furthermore, there is some evidence that the circuitry employed for the monitor system does not respond properly to the short current bursts produced in the various arc discharge sources. It is concluded that if analytical accuracy is to be improved, the monitor system should be placed right at the ion-sensitive plate, and the circuitry modified to deal adequately with short pulses. As a partial solution, the rare platinum isotope ^{190}Pt (abundance 0.0127%) can be used to determine plate sensitivities without having to resort to very short exposures. For this purpose, a pair of platinum wires is mounted with the sample to be analyzed on the same holders, in such a way that either the platinum wires or the sample can be sparked, one pair at a time. Two or three platinum exposures are made to produce suitable blackening of the ^{190}Pt line, then the sample is run in customary fashion. In the analysis, all concentrations are referred to platinum rather than the matrix material, which avoids the use of very short exposures.

(d) Detector. The importance of the character of the lines recorded on the plate has already been mentioned above, and the contributing factors briefly enumerated. Since there occur unavoidable changes in operating conditions, these will result in lack of reproducibility from exposure to exposure. In particular, it is virtually impossible to keep the discharge from moving about between the electrodes, unless one deals with fine wires that are sparked end to end. Even in this most favorable case the electrodes

References p. 53

have to be moved continuously as they are consumed. Frequently it is found that the singly-charged matrix lines are broad and fuzzy, sometimes appearing as multiple lines, even though all other lines are of satisfactory sharpness. Space-charge effects in the main beam, and/or insulating deposits in the neighborhood of the trajectory are believed to be responsible for this situation. If all lines are broad, this can usually be ascribed to instabilities in the supplies for the electric and magnetic fields, or to incorrect positioning of the plate in the magnet gap.

The many errors associated with the plate itself, particularly sensitivity fluctuations caused by variations in the thickness of the gelatine layer covering the active silver bromide crystals, changes in development conditions, etc., will be taken up in detail in the following Chapter.

(vii) Conclusions

It has been shown in the Section above that the quantitative aspects of solids analysis by mass spectrometry still leave much to be desired. Ion yields can be computed only for the simple case of thermal vaporization, but must be determined experimentally for all other systems. The great influence of ion source and analyzer geometry on relative ion currents should not be underestimated. Relative sensitivity coefficients of individual elements, needed for analyses without calibration samples, have, to date, not yet been determined or computed with any precision. Finally, attention has been focused on the various errors existing in sample, source, analyzer, and detector which limit the fidelity with which signals recorded by the detector represent impurity concentrations in the sample.

ACKNOWLEDGMENT

It is a pleasure to acknowledge the collaboration of J. R. WOOLSTON and S. S. GLASS in some of the original work reported here, and also to thank Mr. GLASS for the design of the triggered low-voltage circuitry. The author is grateful to E. M. BOTNICK and H. H. WHITAKER for competent assistance on many occasions.

REFERENCES

1 A. J. DEMPSTER, *Nature*, 135 (1935) 542; *Rev. Sci. Instr.*, 7 (1936) 46.
2 H. W. WILSON AND N. R. DALY, *J. Sci. Instr.*, 40 (1963) 273.
3 R. K. WEBSTER, in A. A. SMALES AND L. R. WAGNER (Editors), *Methods in Geochemistry*, Interscience, New York, 1960, pp. 203–246.
4 I. LANGMUIR AND K. H. KINGDON, *Proc. Roy. Soc.*, London, 107 (1925) 61.
5 M. G. INGHRAM AND W. A. CHUPKA, *Rev. Sci. Instr.*, 24 (1953) 518.
6 H. VOSHAGE AND H. HINTENBERGER, *Z. Naturforsch.*, 14a (1959) 216.
7 R. E. HONIG, in J. P. CALI (Editor), *Trace Analysis of Semiconductor Materials*, Pergamon, Oxford, 1964, pp. 169–205.
8 W. M. HICKAM, *Phys. Rev.*, 74 (1948) 1222A; *ASTM Bull.*, 149 (1953) 17.
9 R. E. HONIG, *Anal. Chem.*, 25 (1953) 1530; *J. Chem. Phys.*, 22 (1954) 1610/11.
10 W. A. CHUPKA AND M. G. INGHRAM, *J. Phys. Chem.*, 59 (1955) 100.
11 J. WOLFF, *Exptl. Tech. Physik*, 9 (1963) 407.
12 P. GOLDFINGER, *Ninth Annual Conference on Mass Spectrometry, Chicago, 1961*, Paper 1.
13 R. P. BURNS, A. J. JASON AND M. G. INGHRAM, *J. Chem. Phys.*, 40 (1964) 1161, 2739; R. P. BURNS AND A. J. JASON, *Twelfth Annual Conference on Mass Spectrometry, Montreal, 1964*, Paper 15.
14 R. H. PLUMLEE, private communication, 1951.
15 C. H. LEIGH, *Report RAD-TR-62-19*, Avco Corp., 1962.
16 R. E. HONIG AND J. R. WOOLSTON, *Appl. Phys. Letters*, 2 (1963) 138.
17 R. E. HONIG, *Appl. Phys. Letters*, 3 (1963) 8.
18 J. BERKOWITZ AND W. A. CHUPKA, *J. Chem. Phys.*, 40 (1964) 2735.
19 R. E. HONIG, *J. Appl. Phys.*, 29 (1958) 549; see also R. M. ELLIOTT (Editor), *Advances in Mass Spectrometry*, Vol. 2, Pergamon, Oxford, 1963, pp. 25–37.
20 R. C. BRADLEY, *J. Appl. Phys.*, 30 (1959) 1; R. C. BRADLEY, A. ARKING AND D. S. BEERS, *J. Chem. Phys.*, 33 (1960) 764; R. C. BRADLEY AND E. RUEDL, *J. Appl. Phys.*, 33 (1962) 880.
21 H. E. STANTON, *J. Appl. Phys.*, 31 (1960) 678.
22 H. J. LIEBL AND R. F. K. HERZOG, *J. Appl. Phys.*, 34 (1963) 2893.
23 R. CASTAING AND G. SLODZIAN, *J. Microscopie*, 1 (1962) 395; *International Conference on Mass Spectrometry, Paris, 1964*.

24 A. J. Smith, L. A. Cambey and D. J. Marshall, *J. Appl. Phys.*, 34 (1963) 2489.
25 L. Cranberg, *J. Appl. Phys.*, 23 (1952) 518.
26 W. S. Boyle, P. Kisliuk and L. H. Germer, *J. Appl. Phys.*, 26 (1955) 720.
27 L. I. Pivovar and V. I. Gordienko, *Soviet Phys. – Tech. Phys.*, 3 (1958) 2101; 7 (1963) 908.
28 M. Goldman and A. Goldman, *J. Phys. (Paris)*, 24 (1963) 303.
29 D. J. DeGeeter, *J. Appl. Phys.*, 34 (1963) 919.
30 R. P. Little and W. T. Whitney, *J. Appl. Phys.*, 34 (1963) 2430.
31 D. Alpert, D. A. Lee, E. M. Lyman and H. E. Tomaschke, *J. Vacuum Sci. Technol.*, 1 (1964) 35.
32 I. Brodie, *J. Appl. Phys.*, 35 (1964) 2324.
33 L. V. Tarasova and A. A. Razin, *Soviet Phys. – Tech. Phys.*, 4 (1960) 879.
34 S. Schwabe, *Z. Angew. Phys.*, 12 (1960) 244.
35 R. E. Honig, S. S. Glass and J. R. Woolston, *Proc. Sixth Intern. Conf. on Ionization Phenomena in Gases, Paris, 1964*, Vol. 2, pp. 209–216.
36 J. Franzen, *Z. Naturforsch.*, 18a (1963) 410.
37 J. Franzen and H. Hintenberger, *Z. Naturforsch.*, 18a (1963) 397.
38 W. M. Hickam and G. S. Sweeney, *Twelfth Annual Conference on Mass Spectrometry, Montreal, 1964*, Paper 41.
39 J. R. Woolston and R. E. Honig, *Rev. Sci. Instr.*, 35 (1964) 69.
40 J. R. Woolston and R. E. Honig, *Twelfth Annual Conference on Mass Spectrometry, Montreal, 1964*, Paper 57.
41 V. S. Venkatasubramanian and H. E. Duckworth, *Can. J. Phys.*, 41 (1963) 234.
42 K. D. Schuy and H. Hintenberger, *Z. Naturforsch.*, 18a (1963) 95, 926.
43 F. Rau and H. Ewald, *Z. Anal. Chem.*, 197 (1963) 106.
44 E. B. Owens and N. A. Giardino, *Lincoln Laboratory Report ESD-TDR-63-584*, 1963.
45 L. A. Cambey, *Report ML-TDR-64-75*, 1964.
46 J. S. Halliday, A. Harrison and A. Riddoch, *Twelfth Annual Conference on Mass Spectrometry, Montreal, 1964*, Paper 56.
47 K. Habfast, *Twelfth Annual Conference on Mass Spectrometry, Montreal, 1964*, Paper 73.
48 R. J. Conzemius and H. J. Svec, *J. Sci. Instr.*, (in press).
49 K. D. Schuy and J. Franzen, talk presented at the Bad Nauheim Meeting of the German Physical Society, 1964.
50 W. D. Davis and H. C. Miller, private communication, 1965.
51 H. Hendel, private communication, 1965.

52 J. Franzen, K. D. Schuy and H. Hintenberger, *Twelfth Annual Meeting on Mass Spectrometry, Montreal, 1964*, Paper 39.
53 J. S. Halliday, P. Swift and W. A. Wolstenholme, *International Conference on Mass Spectrometry, Paris, 1964*, .
54 P. R. Kennicott, private communication, 1964.
55 S. S. Glass, private communication, 1965.
56 R. M. Elliott, R. D. Craig and G. A. Errock, *Proc. International Instrument and Measurement Conference, Stockholm; 1960*, p. 271.
57 J. R. Woolston, private communication, 1964.
58 A. J. Ahearn, *Eleventh Annual Conference on Mass Spectrometry, San Francisco, 1963*, Paper 42.
59 R. Brown, private communication, 1965.
60 E. B. Owens and N. A. Giardino, *Ann. Chem.*, 35 (1963) 1172.
61 B. B. Goshgarian and A. V. Jensen, *Twelfth Annual Conference on Mass Spectrometry, Montreal, 1964*, Paper 52.
62 F. Aulinger, private communication, 1963.
63 M. S. Chupakhin and G. G. Glavin, *Zh. Analit. Khim.*, 18 (1963) 618 (transl. by Asso. Tech. Services, East Orange, N. J.).
64 H. Kawano, *Bull. Chem. Soc. Japan*, 37 (1964) 697.
65 E. Burlefinger and H. Ewald, *Z. Naturforsch.*, 16a (1961) 430.
66 W. Rudloff, *Z. Naturforsch.*, 16a (1961) 1263; 17a (1962) 414.
67 R. E. Honig, *International Conference on Mass Spectrometry, Paris, 1964*, .
68 J. W. Otvos and D. P. Stevenson, *J. Am. Chem. Soc.*, 78 (1956) 546.
69 N. W. H. Addink, *Z. Anal. Chem.*, 206 (1964) 81.

CHAPTER III

Photographic Emulsions as Ion Detectors in Quantitative Mass Spectrography

EDWARD B. OWENS

Lincoln Laboratory, Massachusetts Institute of Technology, Lexington, Mass., 02173*

1. INTRODUCTION

In this chapter the theory of and difficulties involved in the use of photographic emulsions as ion detectors will be discussed. Since more of our knowledge on this subject has been obtained in the field of mass spectrography it is at times difficult to distinguish between the characteristics of the mass spectrograph and those of the detector. For some, such distinction is unimportant, since with empirical standardization the effects of the source, spectrograph and detector can be combined into correction factors which encompass the total analytical method. However, some separation and examination of the several portions of the analytical system are attempted here in the hope that the discussion will lead to understanding and the understanding to improvement.

It is suggested that as the reader considers this chapter he keep in mind the properties of the ion sources and the influence of the mass spectrograph upon the ion beam as is discussed in Chapter II. In this way the unique properties of the emulsion as ion detector will be more clearly distinguished from the rest of the process.

2. HISTORY

The first detection of rays of positive ions was made in 1886 by

* Operated with support from the U.S. Air Force.

GOLDSTEIN[1] when, in conducting experiments with a perforated cathode, he noticed streamers of light behind the perforations. Subsequent investigations by THOMSON[2] showed that these streamers or rays normally carried a positive charge. THOMSON called the streamers positive rays. As early as 1907, THOMSON[3] was detecting the positive rays with screens of powdered willemite which luminesced when struck by the ions. Photography was first used indirectly when VON DECHEND AND HAMMER[4], in 1910, photographed the luminescent screen. That same year also saw the first direct use of the photographic emulsion as an ion detector when KOENIGSBERGER AND KUTSCHEWSKI[5] put the plate inside the evacuated apparatus and let the ions strike the emulsion. By 1911, THOMSON[6] was using the photographic plate for direct ion detection in his parabola positive ray apparatus.

3. NATURE OF ION DETECTION WITH THE PHOTOGRAPHIC EMULSION

a. Composition of the Emulsion

The usual photographic emulsion consists of a suspension of silver bromide grains in gelatine. This suspension is spread in a thin layer on celluloid or glass to form the photographic film or plates. Plates are generally preferred in mass spectrography because the rigidity of the glass makes it possible to place the emulsion precisely on the focal plane of the instrument. The roles of the two principal components of emulsions will be considered first. Then the process of ion detection with photographic emulsions will be described.

b. The Role of the Gelatine

The gelatine was first thought to serve simply as a means for mechanically suspending the silver bromide grains. The permeability of the gelatine permits the chemical components of the developing solution to reach and react with the bromide crystals

References p. 108

without changing the position of the crystals on the plate. It was later found that the gelatine contains trace impurities of sulfur which play a role in providing the active silver sulfide sensitivity specks. For ion detection, the gelatine plays an important role also in determining the sensitivity of an emulsion by limiting the penetration of the positive ions into the suspension of bromide crystals. As early as 1921 THOMSON[7] realized that the penetration of positive rays into the emulsion was small. He found that the most sensitive plate available at that time was the Schumann plate which contained only enough gelatine to keep the silver bromide grains stuck to the plate.

c. The Role of the Silver Bromide

(i) Formation of the latent image

When either an ion or a photon strikes or passes through a silver bromide crystal, some of the energy of the ion or photon is absorbed by the crystal. If sufficient energy is absorbed, positive holes and conduction electrons are liberated within the crystal. The conduction electrons combine with silver ions through a series of steps to form the latent image specks. It is the accumulation of these latent image specks that makes a silver bromide crystal developable when immersed in the developer solution.[8, 9]

There is some disagreement concerning the process by which the latent image is formed. The two theories most often encountered in the literature appear to be that which GURNEY AND MOTT[11] proposed in 1938 and the later theory developed by MITCHELL in various articles from 1953 through 1957.[12]

(ii) The Gurney–Mott theory

In the GURNEY–MOTT theory[8, 9, 13, 14] the conduction electrons that are liberated within the silver bromide crystal by the absorbed energy diffuse to and are trapped by the silver sulfide specks. These sulfide specks—also known as sensitivity specks—thus become negatively charged. The free silver positive ions, which are always present in silver bromide crystals, migrate to the negatively charged sulfide specks and neutralize the negative charge by precipitation as metallic silver. This process is repeated until enough metallic silver is formed to make the crystal developable. This accumulation of silver is the latent image.

(iii) The Mitchell theory

MITCHELL accepts the idea in the GURNEY–MOTT theory that both electron and ionic conduction take part in the formation of the latent image. MITCHELL's main criticisms of the GURNEY–MOTT theory have been summarized by BARKAS[10]. Since the sulfide specks exist only on the crystal surfaces, the GURNEY–MOTT theory explains the surface latent image but ignores the internal latent image. No mention is made of crystal imperfections. The recombination of the carriers should be more probable than the trapping processes proposed in the GURNEY–MOTT theory. It is unlikely that the uncharged centers such as small groups of silver atoms or silver sulfide "specks" can be effective traps for conduction electrons at room temperatures.

MITCHELL explains his theory in his excellent review paper on photographic sensitivity[9] and in a more recent paper.[15] The theory has also been stated in the book by BARKAS[10]. The MITCHELL theory begins (as does the GURNEY–MOTT theory) with the absorption of energy by the crystal resulting in the liberation of conduction electrons and positive holes. However, the MITCHELL theory states that there are no deep traps for the conduction electrons in the crystal at room temperature and that the adsorbed molecules of silver sulfide form deep, irreversible traps for the positive holes. Consequently, the positive holes are trapped and positive ionic charges appear in the form of mobile silver ions. The shallow traps for conduction electrons which exist at the sulfide specks and at the crystal imperfections are deepened by the proximity of the mobile silver ions. This results in the combination of an electron with a silver ion at the trap. A silver atom is formed and adsorbed at the trap site. MITCHELL calls these single silver atoms situated at trapping sites latent pre-image specks. They are formed at the sulfide specks and at the crystal

References p. 108

imperfections which are occupied by silver ions. The latent pre-image specks are unstable, having a lifetime of between 10^{-5} to 20 sec. Unless these specks undergo further reaction during their lifetime, they can dissociate again into mobile silver ions and conduction electrons and diffuse away from the trapping sites.

The latent pre-image speck is changed into a more stable latent sub-image speck by the acquisition of an additional silver atom. The process of this acquisition can be the absorption of additional energy by the crystal, either from the same ion or from another ion, leading to the liberation of an electron and a positive hole. This causes the formation and adsorption of another silver atom at the site of the latent pre-image speck. Alternatively, the growth of the latent pre-image can be caused by the thermal diffusion and aggregation of mobile silver ions and electrons. A latent sub-image speck consists of a pair of silver atoms located at a trapping site. It has a lifetime of the order of days. The adsorption of additional energy and the continuation of the above processes lead to the formation of a group of three silver atoms. MITCHELL calls this group the latent image speck. Situated at a trapping site, it provides the first deep trap for conduction electrons in the silver bromide crystal. The three atom group will trap a conduction electron, acquire a negative charge and attract a mobile silver ion. The silver ion joins the three atom group and neutralizes its negative charge. Now the four atom group traps another electron and the process continues. The latent image is made of these latent image specks. When these specks accumulate sufficient silver they render the silver bromide crystals developable under the usual developing conditions. Note that in this theory the deep trap for conduction electrons is formed by the group of three or more silver atoms associated with a sensitivity speck. These sensitivity specks are provided by crystal imperfections and the silver sulfide specks. At this point it becomes apparent that the meaning of the term "sensitivity speck" (or "sensitivity center") has changed in recent years. In the GURNEY–MOTT theory this term referred only to the silver sulfide specks. In the MITCHELL theory the term refers to the sulfide specks and the crystal imperfection sites.

(iv) Minimum energy per grain

The minimum amount of energy that must be absorbed by a silver bromide grain to make that grain developable differs somewhat for photon and ion exposures. The band gap of silver bromide is 2.6 eV. The absorption of one photon of visible or near ultraviolet light (about 4500 Å and shorter) is sufficient to raise an electron from the valence band into the conduction band thereby creating an electron-hole pair. According to MITCHELL[15] four light quanta are required to make one silver bromide grain developable provided that each quantum produces a silver atom. Thus it appears that a latent image speck (three silver atoms) combined with one extra silver atom is sufficient to make a grain developable. At a minimum of 2.6 eV required per silver atom, 10.4 eV is the minimum amount of energy that a grain must absorb to become developable. However, in general, the quantum yield is somewhat less that one silver atom per absorbed quantum. WEBB[15a] states that eight quanta are required to make a grain developable. KLEIN[15b] shows that the number of quanta required per grain varies from 4 to some 700 with the peak of the distribution occurring at about 20. This would mean that the average crystal grain must absorb about 52 eV (20 $\times$ 2.6) of light energy to become developable. BARKAS[10] states that 30 eV of energy must be absorbed from photon exposures to make one grain developable.

There is no report in the literature giving direct data on the energy that must be absorbed from impinging ions to produce a conduction electron in silver bromide. VAN HEERDEN AND MILATZ[15c] determined by the crystal counting experiments on gelatine-free silver chloride that to produce one conduction electron in silver chloride the crystal must absorb 42.6 eV of energy from 800 V α-particles and 34.2 eV from 1700 V α-particles. Although these data are for silver chloride, WEBB[8] states that the similarity of silver chloride and silver bromide makes these data meaningful for photographic emulsions.

References p. 108

d. Emulsion Response to Ion Bombardment

(i) With no gelatine covering

In an attempt to understand the total process of ion detection with photographic emulsions it is helpful to visualize the case of an individual ion striking the emulsion surface. The result of this ion-emulsion collision will depend upon the nature of the small area of the surface struck by that particular ion and upon the depth of penetration of the ion into the emulsion. Consider the simple case of the oncoming ion striking directly a silver bromide crystal at the surface of the emulsion and having no covering of gelatine. If the ion has sufficient energy the collision may generate latent images having enough metallic silver to make the grain developable by the mechanism described previously. On the other hand, if the ion does not have the energy needed to make the grain developable, it is possible that the required amount of silver may be accumulated by successive collisions of several ions upon the same crystal. It may be unlikely that this simple case of the totally unshielded grains would be present to a significant degree in commercially prepared films and plates.

(ii) With thin gelatine covering—primary blackening mechanism

A slightly less simple case would be one in which the oncoming ion penetrates the gelatine coating and strikes the silver halide crystal with energy still sufficient to make the grain developable. BRIX[16] has stated that for the thin, gelatine-poor emulsions, this ion-crystal collision is the primary blackening mechanism. If the emulsion layer is no thicker than the effective penetration range of the ions into the emulsion, all of the grains could be made developable by this primary mechanism. However, this is usually not the case in mass spectroscopy. The emulsions used most frequently for mass spectrography have thicknesses much greater than the penetration ranges of the ions.

Data sheets from Ilford Inc. state that the Q emulsions have a high concentration of silver bromide at the emulsion surface. But McCREA's statement[17] that all of the gelatine must be removed to remove all of the developed silver indicates that some of the silver bromide is distributed throughout the gelatine. While no data exist concerning the ion penetration into the Q_2 emulsion, this can be approximated by extrapolation of the curves shown by YAGODA[14], MEES[13] and VON ARDENNE[18]. Although these data are not for the Ilford Q emulsions, the stopping power of the emulsions tested are approximately the same as that of the Q emulsions. These extrapolations indicate a penetration of about 0.2 μ for ions of mass up to 4 a.m.u. with 10 to 20 keV energy, the energy range generally used in mass spectrography. This penetration is in reasonable agreement with the 0.15 μ penetration for 7 keV protons reported by BRIX[16]. Ions of higher mass would have even smaller penetration ranges. A rough idea of the penetration range of heavier ions of 20 keV energy may be obtained from the 300 Å penetration of 20 keV argon ions into calcium fluoride reported by MORBITZER AND SCHARMAN[18a] and the 70 to 200 Å penetration of 26 keV krypton ions into copper reported by LUTZ AND SIZMANN[18b]. With a grain diameter of 0.8 μ and the emulsion thickness of 2.5 μ reported by MCCREA[17] for Q_2 emulsions, it is obvious that many of the grains in the Q_2 emulsion are not within the penetration range for 20 keV ions. Consequently many of the grains will not be affected by the primary blackening mechanism.

(iii) With thick gelatine covering—secondary blackening mechanism

The above discussion leads directly to a third case of ion-emulsion collision, namely the case in which the ion misses the silver bromide grains entirely and is stopped solely by the gelatine. As shown above, this case applies to a large portion of the grains in the Q_2 emulsion when it is bombarded with 20 keV ions. Those grains which are so deep in the emulsion layer that they are beyond the penetration range of the oncoming ions may be rendered developable by an indirect process. BRIX calls this process the secondary blackening mechanism and concludes that it is due to luminescense of the gelatine caused by the ion-gelatine collisions. This light emission must take place near the emulsion surface because of the small penetration range of ions of 20 keV energy.

References p. 108

It is perhaps well to make the point here that the penetration range for ions in silver bromide is not appreciably different from that of ions in gelatine containing no silver bromide. If, as estimated above, the ion penetrates into the emulsion 0.20 μ, the same ion with the same energy would penetrate about 0.28 μ into the gelatine alone, or 0.17 μ into the unshielded silver bromide grain. (These relative ranges were calculated by the method described by WEBB[8] using the atomic stopping powers for 2.07 meV ions also given in WEBB's paper. Although these atomic stopping powers vary with ion energy, it is felt that the ratio of penetration ranges would not be greatly different for the 20 keV ions considered in the present discussion.)

While the limited penetration of the 20 keV ions into the emulsion confines the action of the primary blackening mechanism to grains very near the emulsion surface, it does not so restrict the action of the secondary blackening mechanism. The emulsion is very transparent to the light emitted by the ion-gelatine collision and thus permits the light to affect both the surface grains and the deep lying grains.

(iv) Multiple collisions per grain

Next to be considered is the case in which the ion penetrates a layer of gelatine, strikes a silver halide grain, but does not have enough energy to render the grain developable. As stated previously in this chapter it seems possible that the necessary metallic silver might be accumulated through successive collisions of ions. Each ion would have an energy above that required to liberate a conduction electron-positive hole pair but below that required to make the grain developable. In this case, then, a grain could be made developable by the primary blackening mechanism through the action of a small number of ions instead of a single ion as in the first and second cases described above. This accumulative effect of several ion collisions in close sequence extends the depth at which grains will be made developable by the primary blackening mechanism. But this depth cannot be extended beyond the penetration range of the ion into the emulsion as was true of the effect of the secondary blackening mechanism. The ion must penetrate to and collide with the silver bromide grain to give rise to the primary mechanism. The grains very near the surface may be made developable from the collision of a single ion. The grains which are slightly deeper in the emulsion but still within the penetration range may be made developable by the effect of several ion collisions per grain. Those ions which are beyond the ion penetration range can be altered only by the secondary blackening mechanism.

(v) Multiple collisions per ion

The last case to be considered is the case of an ion having sufficient energy to penetrate farther than the diameter of a silver bromide grain. Such an ion may collide with and make developable several grains, depending upon the ion energy, the emulsion thickness, and the grain density within the emulsion. But to penetrate deeper than the 0.8 μ grain diameter reported for Q_2 emulsions an ion must have at least 100 keV energy (again approximated by extrapolation of the data reported by YAGODA[14], MEES[13] and VON ARDENNE[18]). Consequently it seems safe to assume that this last case of ion-emulsion collisions will not exist in mass spectrography as generally practiced today.

(vi) Minimum number of ions per grain

The number of ions required to render a single grain developable by the primary mechanism depends upon the energy of the ions and the thickness of the gelatine covering the grains. LICHTBLAU[19] states that for 20 keV ions of mass 63 to 200 on Q_3 emulsion, only one ion per grain is required; on Q_1 more than one ion per grain is needed. BRIX[16] states that the ion per grain ratio required for the primary process on Agfa Autolith is of the order of unity for 2.6 to 7.0 keV protons. BRIX AND DEHMELT[21] have reported a required ion to grain ratio of 5 for 5 keV protons on Ilford Q_1 and a ratio of 2 for 17 keV protons on the same emulsion. The data of BURLEFINGER AND EWALD[20] show ion/grain ratios from 1.7 to 3.5 for 25 keV ions on Q_1 emulsion. The secondary

References p. 108

blackening mechanism has been reported by BRIX[16] and BAINBRIDGE[22] to require about 10^5 ions per grain.

(vii) Primary vs. secondary mechanisms

The primary and secondary blackening mechanisms are active simultaneously during an exposure. The primary mechanism will dominate for moderate exposures on those emulsions which have a large portion of their silver bromide grains within the ion penetration range. With increasing exposures, however, the primary mechanism soon alters all of the grains within the ion penetration range and the outer layer of the emulsion becomes saturated. The luminescence caused by the continued ion bombardment continues to reach the grains in the deeper portions of the emulsion and the secondary mechanism becomes appreciable. With emulsions that have more gelatine shielding (or for less energetic ions) the secondary mechanism can be predominant. Fig. 1 shows the response curves drawn by BRIX for Agfa Autolith emulsions showing in order: a threshold, a rising straight line portion for the primary blackening, a flattening of the curve to form something of a plateau at the exposure level at which the

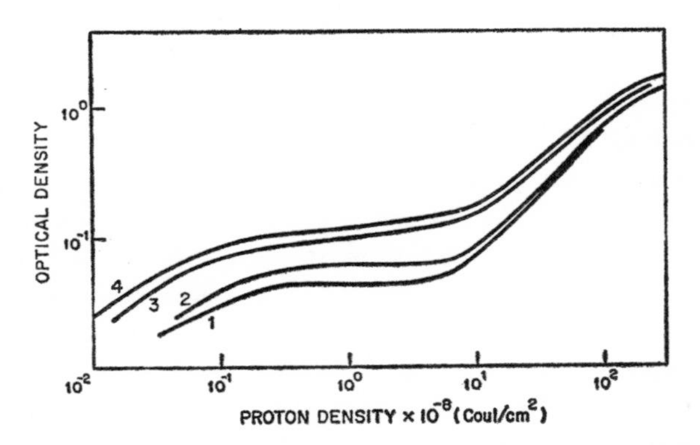

Fig. 1. Complete blackening curves for protons on Agfa Autolith plates. (From P. BRIX, *Z. Physik*, 126 (1949) 35–48.) Curve 1, ion energy 2.6 keV; curve 2, ion energy 3.6 keV; curve 3, ion energy 5.8 keV; curve 4, ion energy 7.0 keV.

primary mechanism has saturated the outer layers, another rising straight line portion caused by the luminescence from the continued ion exposure, and finally another flattening of the curve as the luminescent light saturates the halide grains lying deep within the gelatine. It is clear that emulsions can have response curves varying from the pure ion–grain collision type to a form that is very much like light photography response curves.

It appears that in the use of the Ilford Q emulsions to detect ions of some 5 keV or higher energy, the secondary blackening process can be neglected. The calibration curves for these emulsions do not exhibit any complex structure such as is shown in Fig. 1. As BRIX points out, the simple form of the calibration curve indicates that only one of the blackening mechanisms is contributing to the blackening. BRIX[16] attributed the darkening of Q_3 to the primary mechanism and that of Q_1 to a mixture of the primary and secondary mechanisms. But he[16,21] felt that the contribution from the secondary mechanism on these thin emulsions with ions of 5 keV or higher energy would be too small to be detected.

4. SENSITIVITY AND SENSITIZATION

a. General Principles

As seen from the previous discussion, the response of the photographic emulsion to ion bombardment takes place in three steps. First, the ion penetrates the gelatine to collide with a silver bromide crystal grain; second, the silver bromide grain absorbs energy from the ion; and third, this energy causes the formation of the latent image. Anything done to enhance any of these steps will increase the sensitivity of the emulsion for ion detection.

THOMSON learned quite early that the ions did not penetrate very far into the emulsion. He found that the thin layer, gelatine-poor Schumann plates were the most sensitive plates then available. The Schumann plates were so nonuniform that they could not be used quantitatively[22], and the search continued for other emulsions.

References p. 108

In 1919 ASTON[23] found that the Paget Half Tone plates were both uniform and sensitive, though not as sensitive as the Schumann plates.

On the thin emulsion, gelatine-poor plates the grains protrude from the emulsion with relatively little gelatine between the crystal and the oncoming ion. This results in the most efficient use of ions for making crystal grains developable. Consequently, for thin layers it is safe to say that the larger grained emulsions are the most sensitive for ion detection.

b. Sensitization

(i) Schumannizing

One of the first methods of sensitizing plates for ion detection was to remove much of the gelatine from the plate. ASTON[24] used such a method which had been reported by DUCLEAUX AND JEANTET[25] to increase the sensitivity of Paget Half Tone plates. The removal of the gelatine made the plates quite similar to Schumann plates and so this method of sensitization was called "Schumannizing". ASTON found that Schumannizing did not increase emulsion sensitivity much for light ions but increased it greatly for the heavier ions. This is quite understandable since we now know that the effect of an ion depends on its penetrating power, and it has been shown by BAINBRIDGE[22] that lighter particles penetrate more deeply into the emulsion. The removal of the gelatine would diminish the effect of differing penetrating power and thereby tend to equalize the sensitivity of the emulsion to light and heavy ions. BAINBRIDGE[22] also attempted to sensitize plates by removing the gelatine with dilute sulfuric acid. He too found that the gelatine removal was especially effective for the heavy ions.

(ii) Fluorescent coatings

The literature reveals no successful attempts to increase the efficiency of energy exchange in the direct collision between a charged particle and a silver bromide grain. Instead, the attempts to improve the absorption of energy have been directed at increasing the contribution of the secondary blackening mechanism.

The fact that the luminescence of the gelatine causes blackening leads to the idea that increased sensitivity might be obtained by coating the emulsion with material having especially good luminescent properties. SCHÖNHEIT[26] sensitized Perutz-Perulith and Perutz-Persenso plates by dipping them in a benzene solution of Apiezon oil F. After exposure and before development this oil was removed with pure benzene. The Perutz-Persenso without the Apiezon coating was appreciably more sensitive to light and to the ion beam. This is to be expected since the usual properties of a light sensitive emulsion, namely large grains and low gelatine content, are the same properties that favor ion detection. The primary blackening mechanism apparently dominates in the exposure of this emulsion. After sensitization with the fluorescent oil the Perutz-Persenso was still the more sensitive emulsion, but the gain in sensitivity was greater for the Perutz-Perulith (gain factor of 17 for the Persenso and 76 for the Perulith). This difference in the sensitization effectiveness is also to be expected, since the Perulith depends more upon the secondary blackening process, *i.e.* a luminescent process, and so would be affected more by sensitization which enhances the luminescence.

RUDLOFF[27] used an indirect sensitization technique reminiscent of the detection method of VON DECHEND AND HAMMER[4] used in 1910 in which they photographed a luminescent screen. RUDLOFF made a luminescent screen by coating a clear piece of thin glass with a layer of silver activated zinc sulfide. The photographic film, Agfa Fluorapid X-ray film, was put directly behind the zinc sulfide screen in the plate holder of the mass spectrograph. It was found that the shape and slope of the darkening curve is independent of the mass of the ion; but the intercept of the curve and, therefore, the relative sensitivity are strongly dependent upon mass. At mass two this "sensitizing" system has a sensitivity equal to that of Eastman-Kodak SWR films. The luminescent output decreases sharply with increasing ion mass, and at mass 40 and above, the SWR film is the more sensitive. RUDLOFF states that

References p. 108

this silver activated zinc sulfide is the most efficient producer of light of all known luminescent materials.

When the one to five ions per grain required for the primary blackening mechanism is compared with the 10^5 ions per grain required for the secondary mechanism it appears unlikely that sensitizing can increase the contribution of the secondary to a significant level in a thin layer emulsion. This type of sensitization may increase the response of the thick emulsions in which ion detection depends upon the secondary blackening mechanism, but again the relative efficiencies of the two processes make it appear that the thick emulsions sensitized in this manner will still be much less sensitive than the thin emulsions.

(iii) Chemical sensitization

(a) Sulfide sensitization. The efficiency with which a silver bromide grain uses the absorbed energy to form the latent image can be increased through chemical sensitization. The most commonly used method of chemical sensitization is the addition of sulfur compounds to the suspension during the emulsion production followed by further treatment to form silver sulfide specks. These specks increase slightly the absorption of photon energy, but according to the theory of MITCHELL[9] the principal function of the silver sulfide speck is to provide deep traps for the positive holes that are formed by the absorbed energy. Without these traps the lifetime of the conduction electrons is greatly reduced. The trapping of the holes leaves the crystal in an excited state with an electron in the conduction band and a low-lying unoccupied level corresponding to a positively charged silver sulfide molecule. Because sulfur sensitization enhances the formation of the latent image, this type of sensitization is effective for both photon and ion detection.

(b) Iodide sensitization. Another method of chemical sensitization which should result in improved sensitivity to ion bombardment is the introduction of silver iodide into the silver bromide crystal. The silver bromo–iodide crystals are formed by

coprecipitation upon mixing the silver nitrate and mixed halide solutions. MITCHELL[9] states that the presence of the iodide decreases the band gap of the silver bromide and that the density of the dislocations was higher in the silver bromo–iodide crystals than in pure silver bromide crystals. The higher density of imperfections gives the bromo–iodide crystals a higher density of sensitivity centers and results in greater sensitivity for photons. Since the iodide sensitization increases the efficiency with which the crystal uses the absorbed energy it should be equally effective in sensitizing for ion detection.

(iv) Prefogging

A system of sensitizing that has been used in light photography is to expose uniformly the total surface of the plate to light before making the exposures for the experiment at hand. This pre-exposure serves to bring the exposure level of the total plate to a point just above threshold level and close to the straight line portion of the response curve. With this prefogging the smallest darkening above the fogged level can be measured more accurately. The effect improves the minimum detection limit if the prefogging produces the density level which optimizes the signal to noise ratio, that is, the spectral line to grain fluctuation ratio. The thought that this technique could be applied similarly to ion detection stems from a statement by BAINBRIDGE[22] that for ion detection the effect of exposure of the plate to stray light before use is similar to sensitizing for light photography by prefogging. However, MCCREA[28] reports that prefogging Q_3 emulsion with photons to a density level of 0.016 increased the sensitivity to mass-50 ions only 10%. Prefogging to a density of 0.14 decreased the sensitivity to mass-50 ions to 46% of its original sensitivity. The prefogging to either density level increased the noise by about 57%.

c. *The Effect of Ion Energy on Emulsion Sensitivity*

The effect of ion energy should be considered in terms of the discussion presented in Section 3.d. There we learned that some

References p. 108

threshold energy is required to produce an electron-hole pair in silver bromide. If every electron-hole pair created led to the production of a silver atom, a minimum of four times the threshold energy must be absorbed by a grain to produce the four silver atoms required for developability. This energy required for developability does not include the energy lost by the ions in penetrating the gelatine that covers the grains in commercial emulsions. The magnitude of the sum of the energy for developability plus the energy lost to the gelatine is suggested by the data of BARKAS[10] who found that an energy of at least 500 eV is required to produce a developable grain in nuclear track emulsions.

It is obvious that ions having insufficient energy to penetrate the gelatine would cause no darkening by the primary mechanism. On the other hand, ions with the high energy may penetrate the gelatine, make one grain developable, and expend any excess energy in that grain or in the emulsion or glass on the far side of the grain. However, the Q emulsions have grains distributed throughout a gelatine layer and the thickness of the gelatine covering the grains varies from almost zero up to a thickness much greater than the penetration range of 20 keV ions. The penetration range increases with increasing ion energy thereby increasing the number of grains per unit surface area lying within the domain of the primary blackening mechanism. Thus the sensitivity of the emulsion will increase as the energy increases. Since the Ilford Q emulsions have a high concentration of silver bromide near the surface, the effect of increasing energy and penetration range will drop off markedly once the penetration range exceeds the thickness of the silver bromide rich surface layer.

The relationship between the emulsion sensitivity and the energy of the bombarding ion has been investigated by various workers[16, 20, 21, 22, 29, 30, 31]. KINOSHITA[30] placed absorbing foils between the ion source and the photographic plate. Without intervening foils the ions had sufficient energy to penetrate the entire emulsion thickness. The first eight foils put between the source and the emulsion had no effect on the darkness of the image obtained for exposures of constant duration. This indicated that the energy of the ions after passage through eight foils was still enough to penetrate the entire thickness of the emulsion. Beginning with the ninth foil each successive foil added decreased the darkness of the image proportionally. A plot of the number of foils—after the eighth foil—against the density of the image formed a straight line. This means that the density is linearly dependent upon the ion energy. BRIX[16] reports that for protons on Agfa-Autolith the sensitivity increases with ion energy in the range of 2.6 to 7.0 keV. BAINBRIDGE[22] states that if the energy effect is simply a matter of penetration into the emulsion, the density should be proportional to the range and thus proportional to $(V/M)^{3/2}$ where V and M are the energy and the mass of the ions respectively. However, since his data showed the density varying with the 4.2 power of the energy, BAINBRIDGE concluded that factors other than penetration contribute to the blackening of some emulsions. BRIX AND DEHMELT[21] report the relationship $-\ln(1-W) = aE^x$ where W is the probability that a colliding ion will darken a given grain, E is the ion energy, and x lies between 0.5 and 0.8. The data of OWENS AND GIARDINO[29] indicate that the photographic response of the Q_2 emulsion is directly proportional to the ion energy. BURLEFINGER AND EWALD[20] find that for Ilford Q_1 plates the sensitivity is related to the penetration of the ion into the emulsion and increases monotonically with increasing energy until the maximum sensitivity is reached. WAGNER[31] reports empirical relationships between ion energy and mass and the sensitivity of Ilford Q and Agfa-Schumann plates. WAGNER uses the term f^* for the effective collision cross section of the grain and states that it is proportional to the emulsion sensitivity. The relationship for Q emulsions is given

$$f^* = \frac{5.4 \times E^{0.33}}{1 + \dfrac{1.83\,M}{E^{1.37}}} \times 10^{-9}\ \mathrm{cm^2/ion}$$

and for the Agfa-Schumann emulsion

$$f^* = \frac{1.6 \times E^{0.4}}{1.9\,M^{(1.07 \times E^{0.45})}} \times 10^{-9}\ \mathrm{cm^2/ion.}$$

References p. 108

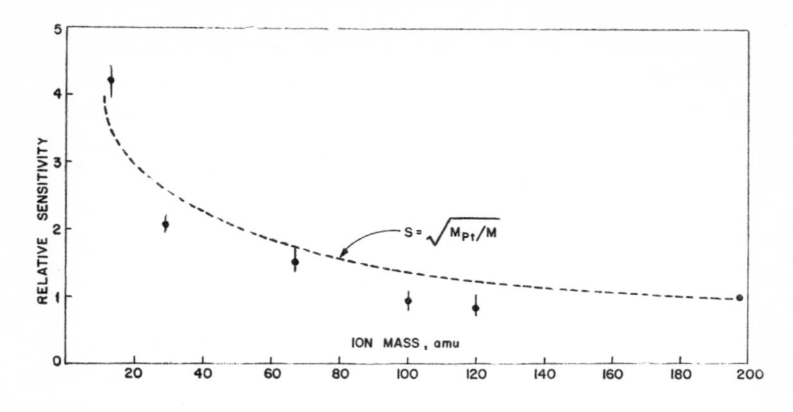

Fig. 2. Emulsion sensitivity *vs.* ion mass. (From E. B. OWENS AND N. A. GIARDINO, *Anal. Chem.*, 35 (1963) 1172.)

d. The Effect of Ion Mass on Emulsion Sensitivity

A number of papers[19, 20, 22, 29, 32] have reported on the effect of ion mass on emulsion sensitivity. BAINBRIDGE[22], working with low energies and thick emulsions, finds that the threshold energy increases in going from low to high masses. BURLEFINGER AND EWALD[20] report that the sensitivity of Q_1 emulsions was proportional to $\left(\frac{2}{M}\right)^{0.5}$. The results of OWENS AND GIARDINO[29], Fig. 2, show that the sensitivity of Q_2 emulsion is approximately proportional to $M^{-0.5}$. The energy-mass sensitivity relationships found by WAGNER[31] are given in Section 4.c. For 17.5 keV ions on Q emulsions, these relationships show that $f_Q{}^*$ is proportional to $35/(25 + M)$† and for Agfa-Schumann $f_S{}^*$ is proportional to $M^{-0.3}$. Both WAGNER[31] and LICHTBLAU[19] report that the slope of the darkening curves for Q emulsions becomes steeper as the ion mass increases. However, this writer's tests for this effect on ions of 15 keV energy indicate that within experimental error the

† The original paper by WAGNER gave the expression for Q emulsions as $35/(25+M)^{-1}$. The –1 exponent in the denominator is obviously a typographical error and has been omitted here.

darkening curves have the same slope for all masses between 29 and 200.

5. RECIPROCITY FAILURE

In mass spectrography exposure times vary from a few seconds to a few hours. In this situation the measuring of relative film darkening to obtain relative exposures assumes that the film response to a given exposure is independent of the time required to accumulate that exposure. That is to say, it is assumed that $E = It$, where E is the exposure, I is the intensity, and t equals the length in time of exposure. This assumption is called the Reciprocity Law; and if it is valid, doubling the time of exposure for a given intensity would have the same effect as doubling the intensity while keeping the exposure time constant. It has long been known that this reciprocal relationship between time and intensity does not hold for many of the emulsions used in light photography. SCHWARZSCHILD[33] found that a general expression for the relationship was $E = It^{\varrho}$. If for a given emulsion ϱ is equal to 1, the reciprocity law is valid. If ϱ is much different from 1 the reciprocity law is said to be invalid, and we have reciprocity failure.

The previous discussion of emulsion blackening caused by ions can now be extended to the consideration of the reciprocity law. As WAGNER[31] has pointed out, for emulsions in which the primary blackening mechanism is predominant, a few ion collisions suffice to make one grain developable. Each of these collisions is much more than sufficient to form the stable latent image specks. Therefore no reciprocity failure should be expected for these emulsions. On the other hand, those emulsions for which the secondary blackening is predominant require thousands of collisions per grain, and reciprocity failure is to be expected. Although BARKAS[10] and CANDLER[34] both propose theories to explain any reciprocity failure that might be seen in the primary blackening process, the latest careful measurements by FRANZEN

References p. 108

AND HEBEDA[35] show that in the Ilford Q emulsions no reciprocity failure occurs. In reviewing papers on this subject, WAGNER[31] reports that all Schumann type and all of the Q emulsions obey the reciprocity law.

6. CHOICE OF EMULSION FOR ION DETECTION

The choice of emulsions to use for ion detection should be based upon the general emulsion characteristics that have been reviewed in this paper. High sensitivity requires large silver halide grains, a low gelatine content, and a thin emulsion layer on the plate. Since the large grains impart a grainy appearance to the spectral lines, a finer grain emulsion might be desired for high resolution work. This better image resolution would be obtained at the expense of some sensitivity. Better uniformity has been achieved generally with medium and fine grain emulsions, but again this is done with the loss of some sensitivity. The choice of the latitude of the emulsion (that is the difference between the threshold and

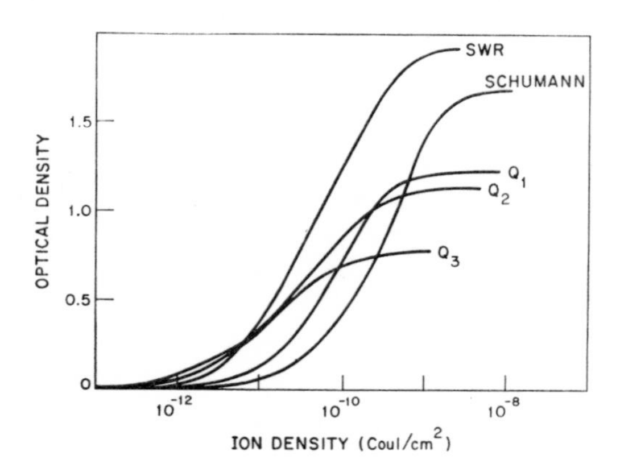

Fig. 3. Absolute darkening curves for ions of mass 2 at 9 keV on SWR, Schumann, and Ilford Q Plates. (From W. RUDLOFF, *Z. Naturforsch.*, 17a (1962) 414.)

the saturation exposure levels) will depend upon the intended use. A wide latitude is desirable for general survey analyses covering many orders of magnitude of concentrations. A smaller latitude with its steeper response curve will give better quantitative results. The single emulsion ideally suited for all purposes cannot be made since some of the desirable characteristics are mutually exclusive. Some of today's emulsions are compromises, and some are designed to favor one characteristic at the expense of the other.

The number of emulsions suitable for ion detection is somewhat limited. A review of mass spectrographic papers published during the past ten years shows only five different emulsions being used. The properties of these five emulsions have been compared in an excellent paper by RUDLOFF[27]. These five emulsions are the three Ilford Q plates, Eastman SWR, and Agfa-Schumann plates. The relative sensitivities of these emulsions as reported by RUDLOFF are shown in Table I. Fig. 3 is a reproduction of the darkening curves Rudloff presented for these emulsions. Tables II and III present some comparative sensitivities of emulsions as summarized by DÖRNENBURG AND HINTENBERGER[36] and INGHRAM AND HAYDEN[37].

The Ilford Q emulsions are by far the most widely used for ion detection today. The Q_1 emulsion has low speed, fine grains, and high contrast; Q_3 has high speed, large grains and low contrast;

TABLE I

DENSITY OF IONS OF MASS 14 AND 9 keV ENERGY REQUIRED TO OBTAIN OPTICAL DENSITIES OF 0.1 AND 0.5 ABOVE BACKGROUND, IN IONS/CM²
(From ref. 27)

Emulsion type	At density = 0.1	At density = 0.5
Q_1	$2.1 \cdot 10^8$	$1.9 \cdot 10^9$
Q_2	$6.8 \cdot 10^7$	$1.5 \cdot 10^9$
Q_3	$4.8 \cdot 10^7$	$9.4 \cdot 10^8$
SWR	$7.0 \cdot 10^7$	$4.6 \cdot 10^8$
Schumann	$4.5 \cdot 10^8$	$3.6 \cdot 10^9$

References p. 108

TABLE II

DETECTION LIMITS FOR IONS OF 5 TO 20 keV ENERGY ON PHOTOPLATES
(From ref. 36)

Emulsion type	Ion	Energy (keV)	Ion density (ions/mm²)	Author
?	Pd^+, Ir^+	12	10^7	RALL
Eastman III-0	X^+	8	10^9	LEWIS AND HAYDEN
Agfa-Autolith	H^+	6	10^9–10^{11}	GEERK AND BRIX
Schumann	H^+	6	10^7	GEERK AND BRIX
Ilford Q_1	X^+	15–20	10^5–10^7	EWALD AND HINTENBERGER
Ilford Q_2	X^+	18	$5 \cdot 10^4$	CRAIG, ERROCK AND WALDRON

TABLE III

RELATIVE SENSITIVITY OF PHOTOGRAPHIC EMULSIONS FOR 10 keV IONS
(From ref. 37)

Emulsion type	Relative sensitivity
Schumann	1.0
Ilford Q_3	0.4
Eastman III-0-W	0.06
Eastman X-Ray	0.02
Eastman SWR	0.3

and Q_2 has properties somewhere between those of Q_1 and Q_3. According to RUDLOFF[27] and FRANZEN AND HEBEDA[35], all three Q emulsions obey the reciprocity law. Despite the popularity of the Ilford Q plates it appears from RUDLOFF's data that the Eastman SWR emulsion may be superior.

Ilford has recently made available new Q emulsions which they state[38] are suitable for low ion exposures and which have lower background fog, higher sensitivity, higher maximum density, and better keeping qualities than the previous unimproved emulsions. These new emulsions completely replace the old Q emulsions which have been discontinued. The new Q_2 emulsion has been tested by GUTHRIE[39], who found that compared with the previously supplied Q_2, the new Q_2 emulsion had lower and more uniform background fog, more contrast, about equal maximum density; and greater dynamic range.

7. DARKROOM PROCESSING

The best general rule about developing plates is to follow the instructions of the emulsion manufacturer, but it should be emphasized that controlled developing procedures are essential for quantitative or even semi-quantitative work. The parameters that must be controlled are the strength and temperature of the developing solution, the duration of development, and the agitation of the plate or solution during development. A paper by this writer[40] describes a simple, homemade apparatus designed to accomplish this control. There are a number of satisfactory plate processors commercially available, although most of the commercial processors are limited to plate lengths up to 10 inches and cannot be used for the 15 inch plates used in some mass spectrographs.

The Ilford Company[41] recommends that the Q plates be developed in ID-19 for 3½ to 5 minutes at 20°C, or in ID-13 for 2½ to 3 minutes at 20°C. Recent work by WOOLSTON[42] shows the effect of increased developing time and temperature on Q_2. WOOLSTON's data show that increasing either the temperature or the developing time shifts the response curve toward lower exposures without markedly changing its slope or shape. The change of developing conditions from 3 minutes at 20° C to 10 minutes at 20° C increased the sensitivity by a factor of 3. Changing from 3 minutes at 20° C to 6 minutes at 24° C also gave a gain of a factor of 3. In both changes there was only a

References p. 108

slight increase in the gamma of the calibration curve. The increase in fog was barely perceptible.

At the time of this writing, FRANZEN, MAURER AND SCHUY[43] at the Max Planck Institute in Mainz are engaged in an investigation of the optimum conditions of plate development. The study includes Ilford ID-13 and ID-19 and Agfa X-Ray Rapid developers used at various temperatures, with various developing times, at full strength and diluted 2 : 1. Their preliminary results indicate that the best results with Q_2 emulsion are obtained with one minute development at 20° C or with two minutes at 16° C in diluted ID-13 (1 part water to 2 parts ID-13). These conditions were best as judged by the line to background ratio.

In general the thin emulsions used for ion detection do not require as much fixing and washing as do the thicker emulsions used for light photography. Ilford recommends that one-third to one-half the fixing and washing times allotted for ordinary plates be used for Ilford Q plates.

KENNICOTT[43a] has used a developing solution that does not include the usual constituents which cause dissolution of the AgBr grain during the developing period. The resultant development makes use of surface latent images only, since the solution does not dissolve the grain to bring the developing chemicals into contact with the latent image within the grain. KENNICOTT suggests that the low energy of the ions in mass spectrography makes it likely that the desired image is almost exclusively at the surface of the silver halide grain. Consequently the surface development would eliminate the results of other image forming processes. The results reported are a marked decrease in the "secondary emission blackening near strong lines", a steeper and more linear characteristic response curve, and an appreciable loss of sensitivity.

8. DENSITOMETRY

The densitometric measurement of the spectrum on the photographic plate is subject to the usual precautions. The densitometer slit should be not wider than one-third the width of the smallest spectral line to be measured. A wider slit would cause an error in the measurement of line width. The rate of scan on the densitometer should be chosen so that the limit imposed by the response time of the recorder does not decrease the peak reading for sharp, dark lines. The appropriate scanning speed can be determined by making repeated scans of a sharp, dark line, increasing the scanning speed one step each scan. All scanning rates will give the same peak value until the response time limitation is exceeded. The fastest scan to be used is the fastest rate that gives a peak deflection that agrees with those obtained with slower scan rates.

A common practice among spectrographers is to set the gain on the densitometer so as to obtain full scale deflection (100% transmission) for the clearest area of the plate. This is valid only for the rather limited case in which the general fog level of the plate is low and is approximately equal to the fog level that existed on the plate from which the calibration data were obtained. When these criteria are not met, the correct technique is to adjust the gain to give 100% transmission for the plate whose transmission is equal to or greater than that of the lowest fog ever encountered on the plates. RUDLOFF[27] used for this purpose an unexposed plate which had been fixed and washed but had not been in the developer solution. A constant setting of the gain for the setting of the zero transmission can be obtained by putting an opaque object in the light path of the densitometer. Use of these constant, reproducible densitometer settings make all of the data compatible regardless of fog level. It is theoretically unsound to attempt to correct for variations in fog and spectral background by varying the densitometer gain to give 100% transmission at the fog or background level. Measuring transmission while varying the densitometer gain is analogous to measuring length with a rubber ruler; increasing the gain stretches the ruler. In addition, the pronounced curvature at the lower part of the response curves makes the analogy one of measuring with a rubber ruler that does not stretch uniformly over its length.

References p. 108

9. EMULSION CALIBRATION

a. Review of Methods

The degree of darkening of a spectral line cannot be used to determine the number of ions producing that line unless the emulsion has been calibrated. It is desirable that the calibration cover the exposure range from barely measurable images to just below film saturation. The data for calibration are usually obtained by putting on a single plate a series of spectral lines having known relative exposure values. LICHTBLAU AND MATTAUCH[44] used a source that generated a steady source of ions, I, and varied the exposure duration t, to obtain the required known variation in exposure $I \cdot t$. This is an excellent method if a steady source of ions is available and if the emulsion obeys the reciprocity law. MATTAUCH AND EWALD[45] used a single exposure of the hafnium isotope pattern. The known relative abundance of the isotopes gave the required relative exposures. There are only six elements with enough isotopes covering the range of abundance desired for this purpose. This method is satisfactory except that it is difficult to cover adequately the full latitude of an emulsion with six or seven points.

It seems to this writer that the above method would be improved by simply making two instead of just one spectra for the calibration data. If one spectrum was made with an exposure 1.5 to 2 times the exposure of the other spectrum, the data would cover the full latitude of the emulsion, and the greater number of points would give greater confidence in the resultant curve.

GEERK AND BRIX[46] and HICKAM AND SWEENEY[47] have used a stepped aperture at the entrance to the magnet section to divide the beam into a number of portions which have known relative intensities. A single exposure made through such an aperture produces spectral lines whose darkening varies in steps which are caused by known intensity ratios. GEERK AND BRIX used this system on a Thomson parabolic spectrograph and calibrated the aperture by measuring with an electrometer the ion beam coming through each aperture step. Without such direct calibration use of the stepped aperture depends upon the assumption that the relative exposures through the aperture steps will be proportional to the step widths. This assumption is subject to some doubt because (a) it assumes that the image width (*i.e.* line width) on the plate remains constant while the aperture width varies by a factor as much as ten, and (b) it assumes that the ion beam is of uniform density over the height and width of the total stepped aperture.

Some workers have obtained their calibration data by using the total ion beam monitor to measure the relative exposure. DÖRNENBURG AND HINTENBERGER[36], finding that their ion beam monitor generally was not precise enough for this, used the relative abundance values of carbon polymers for calibration data. A somewhat similar method first reported by DUKE[48] is based on the two-line technique described by CHURCHILL[49] for use in optical spectrography. The calibration data for the two-line method in mass spectrography are obtained by measuring the lines of two isotopes of a given element in a series of exposures ranging over the total emulsion latitude. The element is chosen so as to have two isotopes with an abundance ratio between 1.2 and 3.0. This writer prefers this two-line method for several reasons. First, as many points as desired can be obtained for the calibration curve by simply having one spectrum for each point. Second, data can often be extracted from the spectra of the sample being analyzed. Third, reciprocity law validity is not required. Fourth, the two-line method based on isotope ratios avoids the use of molecules. The use of isotopes rather than molecules as in the DÖRNENBURG AND HINTENBERGER method[36] is preferred in order to avoid the possible difficulty that might arise if the molecules disintegrate into smaller molecules or atoms upon striking the emulsion as suggested by WAGNER[31]. In addition the use of molecules as described by DÖRNENBURG AND HINTENBERGER overlooks the possibility that charge exchange collisions might add to the intensity of one of the lines used for calibration.

b. The Churchill Two-Line Method

The first step in calibrating an emulsion by this two-line method is to photograph a series of about twelve spectra of a selected element ranging from just detectable to nearly saturated lines. The selected element should have two isotopes with relative abundances between 1.2 and 3.0. The plate should then be developed and the lines for these isotopes measured on the densitometer in the same manner that the sample spectra will be treated. The spectra used for this calibration should be relatively free of fog and background. The precautions noted in Section 8 should be observed in making the densitometer measurements.

A preliminary curve is constructed from the densitometer data by plotting for each spectrum that $\%T$ of the stronger line as abscissa against the $\%T$ of the weaker line as ordinate on log-log paper. This is illustrated in Fig. 4 using data for ^{121}Sb (stronger line) and ^{123}Sb (weaker line).

The data for the calibration curve are obtained from the

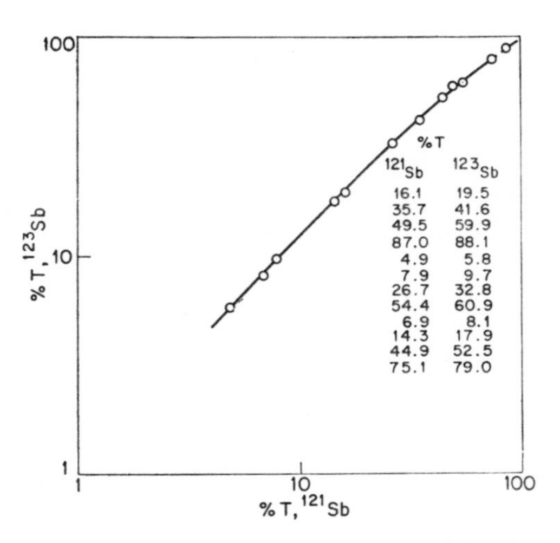

Fig. 4. Preliminary calibration curve, two-line method.

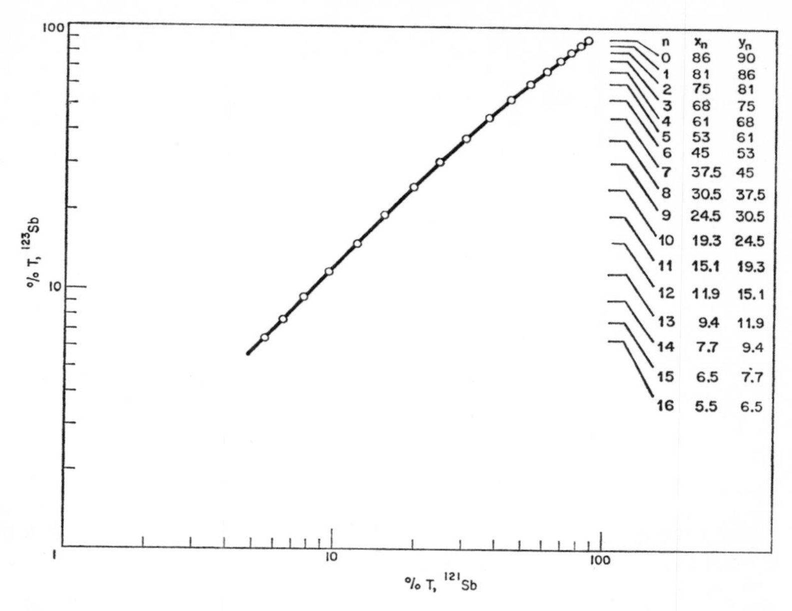

Fig. 5. Use of preliminary curve from Fig. 4 to obtain data for calibration curve.

preliminary curve in the following manner, as illustrated in Fig. 5. Choose a point on the preliminary curve representing the largest $\%T$ value to be used in the subsequent analyses. Call this point 0 and label its coordinates x_o, y_o. Now choose another point (call it Point 1) on the preliminary curve such that the abscissa of Point 0 is equal to the ordinate of Point 1, that is $x_o = y_1$. Select Point 2 such that $x_1 = y_2$. Continue this process always choosing $x_{n-1} = y_n$ and listing the coordinates of each point until the coordinate values are lower than any $\%T$ value to be used in the subsequent analyses. Now construct a table as illustrated in Fig. 6. For the first column list the number n of each point starting with 0 for Point 0. In the second column list the values of r^n, where r is the abundance ratio of the two isotopes being used in the calibration. In the third column give the y_n values. The significance of this table should now be apparent. The second column is a list

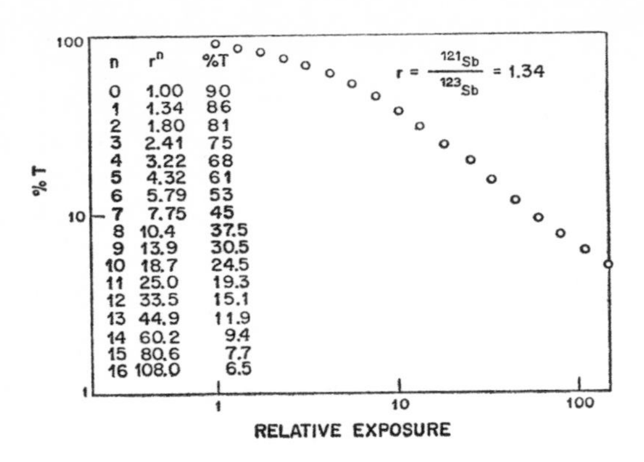

n	r^n	%T
0	1.00	90
1	1.34	86
2	1.80	81
3	2.41	75
4	3.22	68
5	4.32	61
6	5.79	53
7	7.75	45
8	10.4	37.5
9	13.9	30.5
10	18.7	24.5
11	25.0	19.3
12	33.5	15.1
13	44.9	11.9
14	60.2	9.4
15	80.6	7.7
16	108.0	6.5

Fig. 6. Final calibration curve, two-line method.

of relative exposure values with the value of 1 arbitrarily assigned to the lightest exposure and with each successive exposure a factor of r heavier than its predecessor. The third column is the list of $\%T$ values for the exposure listed in column two.

The calibration curve is obtained by plotting on log–log coordinates the $\%T$ values as ordinate against the exposure values as abscissa. Fig. 6 gives an example of a calibration curve plotted from the values obtained from Fig. 5.

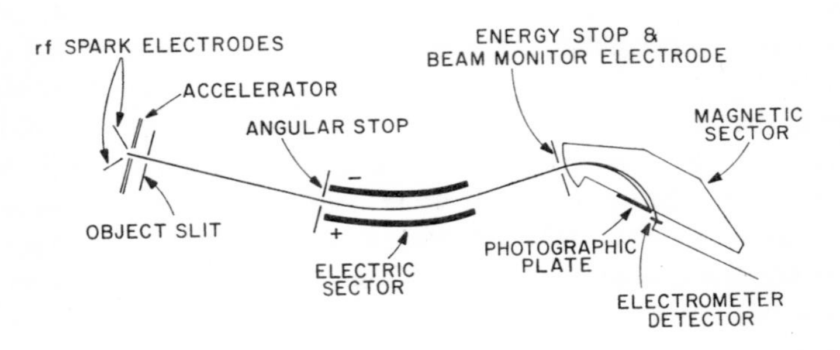

Fig. 7. Simultaneous electrometric and photographic ion detection. (From E. B. Owens and N. A. Giardino, *Anal. Chem.*, 35 (1963) 1172.)

c. *Absolute Calibration*

All of the above calibration methods show the relationship between relative exposure and film response. Any of these methods can be made absolute if the absolute number of ions forming one of the spectral lines can be determined accurately. A method for making this measurement is illustrated in Fig. 7. The apparatus permits the electrometric measurement of one isotope of a given element while another isotope of the same element falls upon the photographic plate.

10. THE RELATIONSHIP BETWEEN EXPOSURE AND EMULSION DARKENING

a. *Theoretical Relationships*

The relationship between the optical density of an image and the density of silver grains in that image can be stated rather simply for an emulsion which consists of a single layer of grains. Assume that the darkened grain is opaque and has an average geometric cross section f_o. The darkened area per cm^2, A_d, will be given by the equation $A_d = N_d f_o$, where N_d is the number of darkened grains per cm^2. Since the fraction of light that is blocked by the image equals the fraction of the image area that is occupied by darkened grains, we see that the darkening, S, is proportional to the number of darkened grains per cm^2, that is, $S = N_d f_o$. In the usual densitometry terms, the definition of the darkening is given as $S = I_b/I_o$; and transmission, T, is defined $T = I_t/I_o$, where I_b is the amount of light that is blocked by the image, I_t is the amount of light that is transmitted through the image, and I_o is the incident light. Obviously, from these definitions $T = 1 - S$, and the relationship between T and the number of darkened grains is $T = 1 - N_d f_o$.

Optical density, D, is defined $D = \log (1/T)$, and it follows that the relationship between the optical density and the density of

References p. 108

silver grains is expressed by the equation $D = \log [1/(1-N_d f_o)]$.

To express the relationship between the exposure and the number of grains hit by the ion bombardment, WAGNER[31] uses the Poisson equations,

$$W_n = 1 - e^{-f_o x} \sum_{0}^{n-1} {}_i \frac{(f_o x)^i}{i!}$$

where W_n is the probability that a given grain is hit n times, f_o is the geometric cross section of the grain, and x is the number of ions per cm^2 that hit the plate during that exposure. In the simple case of the single grain layer with the gelatine covering so thin that one ion collision is sufficient to make the grain developable, the above equation can be simplified to $W_1 = 1 - e^{-fx}$, and W_1 is now the probability that a given grain will be made developable by the exposure, and f_o has been replaced with f, the average effective cross section of the grain. This change must be made because the effective cross section of the grain depends upon the energy of the ion and the thickness of the gelatine covering the grain. The number of grains per cm^2 that will be hit and made developable, N_d, then will be $N_d = N_o (1-e^{-fx})$. Since $S = fN_d$ and $S_{max} = fN_o$, we get $S = S_{max}(1-e^{-fx})$. WAGNER[31] states that this is equivalent to the equation $D = D_{max}(1-e^{-fx})$ that was proposed and verified by KINOSHITA[30] for the single collision darkening on a single grain layer emulsion.

However, it has been pointed out in Section 3.d.vi that the primary blackening mechanism is not limited to the single collision case, but can be the result of several successive collisions. In view of this fact WAGNER gives the Poisson equation in the form

$$W_{1,2,3}\cdot = 1 - e^{-fx} \left[1 + (1-\alpha) fx + (1-\beta) \frac{(fx)^2}{2}\right]$$

from which we get

$$S = S_{max} \left\{1 - e^{-fx}\left[1 + (1-\alpha) fx + (1-\beta) \frac{(fx)^2}{2}\right]\right\}$$

with $0 \leq \alpha \leq 1$ and $0 \leq \beta \leq 1$, and where α and β are the probability functions for the appearance in the emulsion darkening of the single and double collisions.

b. Empirical Relationships

Other workers have related exposure and emulsion darkening on an empirical basis. Most of the empirical relationships reported are simply best fits of data to a curve. HULL[50] reports that the data for Ilford Q_2 plates exposed to 15 keV ions obey closely the relationship

$$E_x = \left(\frac{1-T_x}{T_x-T_\infty}\right)^{1/R}$$

McCREA[51] reports that a nearly linear plot is obtained when log exposure is plotted against *Tm*, where *Tm* is the *T* value after transformation via a probability deviate function. The transformation can be eliminated by plotting the *T* values directly on log-probability graph paper. The bases for preference among these empirical relationships are ease of handling, either graphically or mathematically, and for computer use, the closeness of the fit of the experimental data to the assumed mathematical relationship.

TABLE IV

ARBITRARY DENSITY EXPRESSIONS AND USEFUL RANGES. L_0 AND L ARE AMOUNTS OF INCIDENT AND TRANSMITTED LIGHT RESPECTIVELY

(From ref. 52)

Density expression	Useful range, %T of line
$D_1 = \log L_0/L$	10 to 50
$D_2 = \log (L_0-L)/L_0$	60 to 100
$D_3 = (L_0-L)/L_0$	20 to 80
$D_4 = \log (L_0-L)/L$	10 to 100
$D_5 = (L_0-L)/L$	0 to 20

References p. 108

WOOLSTON[42] has used the equation reported by HULL in a computer program which converts relative transmission measurements into concentrations.

KAWANO[52] has used five different expressions for line "density" in plotting "density" *versus* exposure. The expressions are shown in Table IV. The choice of which "density" to use is governed by the blackening range in which the plot of "density" *versus* exposure gives a straight line. The optical density range of this "useful range", *i.e.* the straight line portion, is given in Table IV for each "density" expression.

11. QUALITATIVE SPECTRUM ANALYSIS

a. Identification

The subject of spectral identification will be discussed but briefly in this chapter since it is not a problem that is unique with the use of photographic detection. The general method of determining the ion mass from the spectral position of the line is well known, and the nature of any refinements in the general procedure to obtain higher accuracy depends largely on the particular mass spectrograph being used.

Several tables of isotope masses and mass spectrum lines have been published to assist in the spectrum analysis[53,54,55]. The complexity of the spectra depends to a large extent upon the type of ion source used to generate the ion beam. The r.f. spark is the source with which the photographic plate is most commonly used. Unfortunately, because of the high energies involved in the discharge, the spectra of the ion beams generated in the r.f. spark are among the most complex to be encountered. The ions in an r.f. spark spectrum will produce many lines due to multiple ionization and formation of molecules in addition to the charge exchange collision and isotope distribution lines common to spectra from many ion sources. Multiple ionization produces lines at spectral positions of M/q, ion mass divided by ion charge.

This writer has seen spectra in which lines appear for all values of q up to 16 for monatomic ions. Generally, the number of ions of charge q decreases as q increases, but the rate of decrease varies greatly. OWENS[56] has reported a ratio for X^{+2}/X^{+1} as high as 0.76, and FRANZEN AND HINTENBERGER[57] under other conditions with different samples have obtained a X^{+2}/X^{+1} ratio as low as $1.5 \cdot 10^{-4}$.

Two types of molecules have been seen in r.f. spark spectra-molecules containing isotopes of only one element and molecules containing more than one element. The relative abundances of the single element molecules have been calculated and tabulated in the tables of OWENS AND SHERMAN[54], and CORNU, MASSOT AND TERRIER[55]. However, the darkening of these single element molecule lines may not follow the calculated probabilities because lines due to some charge exchange collisions may coincide with some of the molecular lines. For example, an ion going through the accelerator and electrostatic sections with a +2 charge but suffering a collision that changes its charge to +1 before it traverses the magnet field will cause a line that may coincide with the *dimer* (molecule consisting of two atoms of the same element) of that ion. This line will then be darker relative to other dimer lines. In the normal r.f. spark spectra the single element dimer lines are weaker than the monatomic ion lines by about three orders of magnitude. In general, the abundance of the molecules in the ion beam decreases as the number of atoms in the molecule increases.

Many types of molecules containing two or more elements have been seen in r.f. spark spectra. The major elements have been seen as oxides, hydroxides, dioxides, carbides, dicarbides, hydrides, and in various mixtures with other major elements. Generally, these molecular lines are very light in the spectra.

The relative darkness of charge exchange lines within a spectrum depends upon the gas pressure in the spectrograph and upon the charge distribution of the ions leaving the source. The relative intensities between charge exchange lines can be predicted from the facts that the abundance of an ion in a spectrum decreases

References p. 108

TABLE V

PREDICTED INTENSITY PATTERN AND POSITION FACTORS FOR CHARGE EXCHANGE LINES

X^{a-b} indicates ion traversed electrostatic section with charge a and traversed the magnetic section with charge b, the change from charge a to b being caused by a charge exchange collision occurring between these two sections. The mass position at which the ion will be found is calculated by multiplying the actual ion mass by the factor F.

Decreasing intensity ↓

X^{2-1} $F=2.0$					
X^{3-2} $F=0.75$	X^{3-1} $F=3.00$				
X^{4-3} $F=0.444$	X^{4-2} $F=1.00$	X^{4-1} $F=4.00$			
X^{5-4} $F=0.3125$	X^{5-3} $F=0.555$	X^{5-2} $F=1.25$	X^{5-1} $F=5.00$		
X^{6-5} $F=0.24$	X^{6-4} $F=0.375$	X^{6-3} $F=0.666$	X^{6-2} $F=1.50$	X^{6-1} $F=6.00$	
X^{7-6} $F=0.1944$	X^{7-5} $F=0.280$	X^{7-4} $F=0.4375$	X^{7-3} $F=0.7777$	X^{7-2} $F=1.75$	X^{7-1} $F=7.00$...
. . .					

Decreasing intensity →

with increasing ion charge, and a multiply charged ion is more likely to pick up one electron than two in the charge exchange collision. On this basis the predicted pattern of intensities is given in Table V in which the symbol $X^{2\to 1}$ means that ion X went from a $+2$ to a $+1$ charge in the charge exchange collision, and $F=2$ means that the position of the line in the mass spectrum is found by multiplying the actual mass of the ion by the factor 2. The observed position of a charge exchange line may not coincide exactly with the calculated position because of a small amount of energy loss that may occur in the charge exchange collision.

When these energy losses do occur, the observed lines are displaced toward the lower mass side of the calculated position.

b. Sensitivity

One important aspect of qualitative analysis is the sensitivity of detection. In fact, it is this writer's opinion that qualitative analyses are meaningless without known detection limits. The sensitivity of the photographic detector has been discussed in Section 4. Sensitivity is also important in the quantitative calculations and so will be discussed in Section 12. From these sections we learn that the sensitivity depends on the mass and energy of the ion, on the area of the spectral line, on the background level around the spectral line and, of course, on the nature of the emulsion. Now let us interpret these facts in terms of analytical results. Using the apparatus shown in Fig. 7 (Section 9.c) this writer has determined that with ions of mass of 100 a.m.u. and energy of 15,000 eV, about 10^5 ions per mm^2 are required to make a detectable image in Ilford Q plates—this is the Q_2 emulsion before the recent improvements were made. The lines measured for these ions actually had an area of about 0.1 mm^2. So the minimum detectable line was caused by 10^4 ions landing within the area of the line. If the total number of ions reaching the detector is 10^{13}, this particular line represents 1 part in 10^9 sensitivity. If within the spectrum all of the ions from a given element in the sample fall in this one line, this element can be said to have a one part per billion sensitivity in an exposure of 10^{13} ions. Most elements have several isotopes; and if the most abundant isotope has an abundance of 25%, 4×10^4 ions of that element will be required to put 10^4 ions at the position of the strongest line for the element. This element has a sensitivity of 4 ppb in a 10^{13} ion exposure. It has been shown that the emulsion is more sensitive to lighter ions. Consequently, in a 10^{13} ions exposure boron may have a sensitivity of 0.3 ppb compared with an indium sensitivity of 1 ppb in the same exposure. Since the emulsion darkening depends on the number of ions per unit area

References p. 108

of the plate, it follows that more ions are required to make a wide line detectable than for a narrow line.

All of the above assumes that all elements are ionized with equal efficiency. This assumption is only approximately true, but this problem is not associated with the detector and has been discussed in detail in Chapter II.

12. QUANTITATIVE SPECTRUM ANALYSIS

a. General Remarks

The methods that have been published on analysis of mass spectrograms differ amongst themselves on the degree of refinement and on the approach, theoretical or empirical, taken in making these refinements. Several methods will be described here, from the simplest to the most refined, with some discussion on the effect of the refinements upon the analytical results. It is important to realize that at this point the discussion is concerned only with relating the photograph of spectra of an ion beam to the ionic composition of that beam. And the beam under discussion is the ion beam as it exists when it hits the photographic plate. Therefore, the errors that will be discussed in this section are errors in analyzing the spectra, not errors in analyzing the sample. The relation between the sample and the ion beam at the detector has been discussed in Chapter II and will be discussed briefly in Section 13 of this chapter.

b. Visual Methods

(i) Simple visual method

The simplest method that this writer has seen used to evaluate mass spectra is one in which the ratio of impurity to matrix element is estimated from the ratio of the minimum exposures in which the impurity element and the matrix element are detectable, with appropriate correction for isotope abundance. The required graded series of spectra is made of the sample using the total beam monitor to control the exposures. The series starts with the lowest exposure that the beam monitor is capable of measuring and continues for a succession of some thirteen spectra following the relative exposure pattern of 1, 3, 10, 30, 100, . . . etc. A series of thirteen such exposures covers an exposure range of one to one million. The ratio of the concentrations of the impurity element i to a matrix element m is calculated

$$C_{\mathrm{i}} = C_{\mathrm{m}} \cdot \frac{E_{\mathrm{m}}}{E_{\mathrm{i}}} \cdot \frac{A_{\mathrm{m}}}{A_{\mathrm{i}}}$$

where C_{i} and C_{m} are the concentrations of the impurity and the matrix respectively;

E_{i} and E_{m} are the lowest exposures in which can be detected the singly charged ions of the impurity and the matrix respectively;

A_{i} and A_{m} are the fractional abundances of the isotopes being used to evaluate the impurity and the matrix respectively.

This method is based on the assumptions: (a) the ratio of two elements in the spectra can be estimated from the consideration of just the singly charged ions of these elements, (b) the eye can make the appropriate corrections for line width and background, (c) all singly charged ions have the same detection limit, (d) the minimum detectable exposure varies inversely with concentration, and (e) the total ion beam monitor measures the exposure ratios accurately. Some consideration of the validity of these assumptions is necessary for the evaluation of this method.

The ions of an element form many lines in a mass spectrum and the validity of the first assumption requires that the ions of all elements have the same charge distribution and undergo the same proportion of charge exchange collisions and molecule formation. These factors are obviously functions of the ion source and as such are discussed in detail elsewhere. Owens and Giardino[29] show that with some materials in the r.f. spark ion source, measurements of the singly charged ion lines alone would

References p. 108

result in errors of spectrum analysis of on the average not more than 10%. However, in a later paper OWENS[56] shows that for other materials errors as high as 67% would result from this technique. SCHUY AND HINTENBERGER[58] report that the ion charge distribution is much more constant in the disjunctive d.c. spark than in the r.f. spark.

The ability of the eye to correct for line width is virtually unknown. Theoretically the line width increases with the square root of the mass in the original MATTAUCH–HERZOG double focusing mass spectrograph[59]. If no corrections are made for line width, the amount of error would equal the ratio of the square root of the masses of the two ions being compared. Thus for the determination of boron in lead the line width effect could cause an error of a factor of 4.5.

Unpublished results obtained in this writer's laboratory indicate that to a first approximation the relation of the transmission of a barely visible line, T_p, to that of the background, T_B, is a constant with the value $T_p/T_B = 0.9$. This ratio was determined

TABLE VI

EXPOSURE ABOVE BACKGROUND REQUIRED TO OBTAIN JUST DETECTABLE IMAGE, RATIO OF LINE TO BACKGROUND TRANSMISSION EQUALS 0.9

% Transmission		Corresponding exposure		Exposure above background
Line	Background	Line	Background	
86	95	1.34	0.74	0.6
81	90	1.80	1.00	0.8
45	50	7.8	6.5	1.3
36	40	11.0	9.4	1.6
27	30	16.4	14.2	2.2
18	20	27.1	24.0	3.1
9	10	62.0	54.5	7.5
5	5.5	155	128	27

on Ilford Q_2 emulsion for backgrounds of 95% T to 5% T. Using this relationship and the calibration curve of Fig. 5, the minimum detectable exposure above background was calculated over the total range. These data are shown in Table VI. It is seen that the minimum exposure detectable by eye varies by a factor of 45 when the background varies from 95% T to 5% T.

The assumption that the emulsion is equally sensitive to all ions ignores the effect of ion mass on sensitivity discussed in Section 4.d. Fig. 2 (p. 74) indicated that the mass effect causes the emulsion sensitivity for mass 10 to be about 4.5 times that for mass 200. The effect of ion energy on sensitivity discussed in Section 4.c does not apply to the present discussion because with a constant accelerating voltage all singly charged ions strike the emulsion with the same energy.

The assumption that minimum detectable exposure for an element varies inversely with concentration seems reasonably well supported by the work of CRAIG, ERROCK AND WALDRON[60] and HANNAY AND AHEARN[61]. The question of relative sensitivity and relative concentrations of two elements depends in part upon the characteristics of the source and is discussed elsewhere in this book.

The accuracy with which the total beam monitor measures the relative exposures depends, of course, on the individual instrument. The excessive noise and drift observed on some of the beam monitors make the measurement of small exposures subject to large errors. Unfortunately, these small exposures are necessary in this and other methods which compare "just detectable" lines. In the analyses of gold, for example, exposures ranging from 10^{-7} C to 10^{-13} C would be required to obtain a ratio of one part in one million. Gold has no isotope of low abundance to give a line useful in estimating sensitivity in exposures below 10^{-13} C, and even at 10^{-13} C many monitors exhibit poor dependability. Under these circumstances it would be quite difficult to make reasonably accurate estimates of impurity concentrations at the 1 ppm level and lower. It must be kept in mind also that with the usual series of exposures the choice of just detectable image is being made between exposures that are different by a factor of three.

In summary it appears that the use of the simple visual method can give rise to error factors of as much as 1.7 for the ion charge distribution, 4.5 for the line width variation, 2.2 for backgrounds no darker than 30% T, 4.5 for the mass effect on emulsion sensitivity, 3 because of the ratio between adjacent exposures, and an unknown factor for the ion beam monitor problem. There is no way to know how these various error factors will combine in practice and so no attempt will be made to estimate a total error factor. The total error is probably much smaller than the worst combination of the factors given above. However, the need for refinements is obvious.

(ii) The refined visual method

The visual method for spectrum analysis published by CRAIG, ERROCK AND WALDRON[60] introduces a number of corrections. In this method the concentration of an impurity, C_i, is calculated from the expression:

$$C_i = \frac{E_s}{E_i} \cdot \frac{C_s}{100} \cdot \frac{A_s}{A_i} \cdot \frac{S_s}{S_i} \cdot \frac{W_i}{W_s} \cdot \frac{M_i}{M_s}$$

where E_s is the estimate of the minimum exposure at which an isotope of an internal standard, usually a major constituent present in known concentration, becomes "just detectable",

E_i is the similar estimate of the minimum exposure for an isotope of the impurity element,

C_s is the % concentration of the internal standard,

A_s and A_i are the abundances of the isotopes of the standard and impurity elements, respectively, used for the estimates,

S_s and S_i are the relative sensitivities of the singly charged ions of the standard and the impurity elements,

W_s and W_i are the relative areas of the two mass spectral lines under consideration (for constant line length this factor becomes simply the relative line widths), and M_s and M_i are the ratios of the intensities of the singly charged ions to those of the particular multiply charged ions on which the estimate is based (singly charged ions are used when possible and then M_s and M_i are taken as unity).

When multiply charged ion lines are used the value for M is determined usually in separate experiments from the equation $M = e_q/e_1$, where e_q and e_1 are the exposures necessary to obtain lines of equal density of the ions of charge q and the singly charged ions of the particular isotope used for the concentration estimation.

The W_i/W_s ratio corrects for the variation in line area (or line width when the line length is constant). However, it is difficult to see just how this area or width is estimated without densitometry. For an instrument of the original design of the MATTAUCH–HERZOG double focusing mass spectrograph LICHTBLAU AND MATTAUCH[44] used the ratio of the square root of the masses for this width correction. This assumes that the spectrum is in perfect focus and that no space charge broadening takes place. However, the Robinson modification of the Herzog shunt results in line widths that no longer have a simple relation to the mass. Consequently, for instruments having the Robinson modification, and perhaps for other instruments also, the line areas must be measured before area corrections can be made.

The M_s/M_i ratio is used to correct for ion charge distribution only when multiply charged ion lines are used for the quantitative estimates. When singly charged ion lines are used equal ion charge distribution is assumed for all elements. The possible errors arising from this assumption have been discussed above.

The correction for relative sensitivities embodied in the ratio S_s/S_i combines several factors. Relative ion yield at the source, relative transmission through the instrument and relative sensitivity of the detector for the various ions being measured are all contained in the ratio. These relative sensitivities are usually determined for a given element by comparing analytical results with the established analysis of known standards. Such empirically determined sensitivity factors are most likely not generally applicable but

References p. 108

apply only to the specific case of impurity X in matrix Y as existed in the known standard. A sensitivity value of unity is used when the lack of known standards precludes the determination of empirical sensitivities. This use of unit sensitivity ignores the effect of mass upon emulsion sensitivity.

The corrections introduced in this refined visual method reduce or eliminate the error factor of 1.7 for ion charge distribution if the estimate is made using multiply charged ions. The error factor of up to 4.5 for line area variation is eliminated in some cases. The empirically determined sensitivity factor if used correctly can reduce or eliminate several of the sources of error simply by its empirical nature.

(iii) Visual method using standard samples

JAMES AND WILLIAMS[62] used a visual method for comparing the spectra of analyzed standards and the unknown samples. In determining boron in silica the boron concentration, B_x, of the unknown was calculated with the equation $B_x = B_s(E_s/E_x)$ where B_s is the known boron content of the standard, and E_s is the minimum exposure of the standard in which boron appears, and E_x is the corresponding exposure for the unknown sample. Because of the direct comparison this method eliminates most of the error of the above methods. Except for the difficulty of matching two series of spectra in which the closest exposures differ by a factor three, the accuracy of this method depends principally upon the ability of the ion source to produce equivalent spectra of the standard and the unknown. Obviously, the standards used for this or any other r.f. spark method must be of known composition and must be homogeneous on a microvolume scale.

c. Densitometer Methods

(i) Exposure ratios at equal density

An improvement upon the method using the exposure ratio of the "just detectable" image was made by CRAIG, ERROCK AND WALDRON[60] by using a densitometer and matching line densities.

In this method the optical density of a matrix element line is plotted against the logarithm of the exposure as measured by the total beam monitor. The optical density of the impurity line is measured in one exposure, E_i. The exposure, E_s, required to produce the line of the matrix element at the same density level as the impurity line is read from the above plot. The values of E_i and E_s determined in this way are used in the equation given in Section 12.b.ii. This method eliminates the errors arising from matching by eye two series of spectra in which adjacent exposures differ by a factor of three. Although the authors do not say that they make use of it, the strip chart recording of the densitometer can be used to estimate the relative area values W_i and W_s used in their calculations. Except for these two improvements the method is subject to all of the errors enumerated for the visual method in Section 12.b.ii. The contribution of the background is different in the densitometer method than in the visual method. In the visual method the background affected the minimum detectable exposure, but in densitometry the background adds to the optical density of the line being measured. The CRAIG–ERROCK–WALDRON method as reported in ref. 60 makes no correction for the effect of background on the measured optical density of the lines.

This same approach of using exposure ratios at equal line densities has been used with slight modification by PERKINS AND POLLACK[63]. The modification consisted of plotting line density *versus* exposure for the matrix element and for each impurity element. The values for exposure in these plots are the readings of the total beam monitor. A density value lying in the mid-part of the straight line portion of the above curves is taken for the density at which the relative exposures will be read. A line is drawn across the chart containing these curves at the chosen density level and parallel to the exposure axis of the plot. The exposure value for each element is taken as the intercept of the curve for that element and the equal density line just drawn. The ratios of these exposure values are taken as the concentration ratios. PERKINS AND POLLACK corrected this concentration ratio for the effect of beam spread during passage through the magnet and suggested that a correction be made for the effect of ion mass on emulsion sensitivity.

(ii) Methods with emulsion calibration

DUKE[48] reports a method that makes use of an emulsion calibration curve obtained by the Churchill two-line method explained in Section 9.b. The densities of the impurity lines and the matrix lines are converted to relative beam intensities by means of the calibration curve. The ratios of these beam intensities are corrected for the ratios of the exposures in which the lines are measured, for the isotopic abundances of the elements involved, for the relative sensitivity of the detector to the ions being measured, and for the relative line areas as approximated by the $\sqrt{M}$ function explained above. The ratio of beam intensities corrected in this manner is taken to be equal to the concentration ratio. In essence this method is very similar to the CRAIG–ERROCK–WALDRON method. The area correction is based on a theoretical relationship which assumes perfect focusing and no space charge broadening, the relative sensitivity correction combines several effects, and no background correction is made. The method of DUKE makes no correction for possible variations in ion charge distribution.

DESJARDINS, STEFANI, BOURGUILLOT AND CORNU[64] report a method which is essentially the same as the PERKINS–POLLACK method (Section 12.c.i) except that the DESJARDINS group converted line density values to intensity values via an emulsion calibration curve. The intensity values were then plotted against exposure and the exposures compared at one intensity level. The DESJARDINS group corrected for line area by assuming that the line increased with the square root of the mass.

The method developed by this writer[29] attempts to make corrections for all sources of error or analytical bias. Emulsion response is determined by the Churchill calibration method, the lines are measured on a densitometer giving both intensity values and line width correction data, background corrections are made,

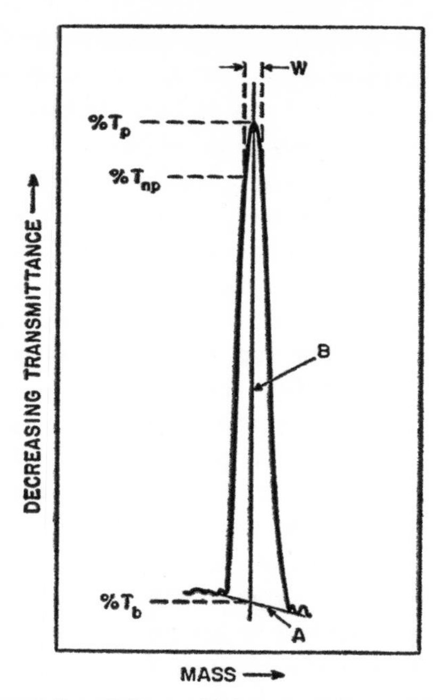

Fig. 8. Background and line width corrections. (From E. B. OWENS AND N. A. GIARDINO, *Anal. Chem.*, 35 (1963) 1172.)

TABLE VII

DATA TREATMENT
(From ref. 29)

Line	$\%T_p$	$\%T_b$	I_p	I_b	$I_c = I_p - I_b$	$\frac{1}{2}I_c$	$\frac{1}{2}I_c + I_b$	$\%T$ at $\frac{1}{2}I_c + I_b$	W	$N = I_c \cdot W$
1	10.3	95.5	52.5	0.8	51.7	25.9	26.7	18.4	5.9	305

corrections are made for the effect of ion mass and energy on emulsion sensitivity, and ion charge distribution is taken into account. These calculations are illustrated in Fig. 8 and Table VII.

References p. 108

$\% T_p$ and $\% T_b$ are the transmission data for the line peak and line background, respectively. I_p and I_b are the ion density values corresponding to the $\% T$ values as determined from the calibration curve. $I_p - I_b = I_c$ gives the peak ion density corrected for background. To assume that I_c is proportional to concentration would be neglecting the line area. To use simply the ratio of line widths for this correction is to assume that the ions are uniformly distributed over the width of the line. These difficulties can be avoided by replotting the line profile in terms of ion density, I, across the width of the line and integrating the area under this line profile. In place of this time consuming procedure, the replotting and integration is reasonably well approximated by multiplying the peak ion density corrected for background by the width of the line profile at a transmission level equivalent to one half the peak ion density. In the illustration, I_c is divided by 2 and then the ion density of the background is added to get the value for one half peak ion density above background, $(I_c/2) + I_b$, for which the $\% T$ value is now determined from the calibration curve. At this $\% T$ value the width of the line profile is measured directly on the recorder trace from the densitometer. Multiplying this width by the peak ion density, $I_c \cdot W = N$ gives a reasonable approximation of the replotting and integration mentioned above. N is the apparent yield and is proportional to the number of ions forming the spectral lines. The term apparent yield is used since this value must be corrected for the effect of ion energy and mass.

The correction for ion energy is based on the author's findings (see Section 4.c) that the emulsion sensitivity is directly proportional to the ion energy. The correction is accomplished by dividing the apparent yield, N, by the charge on the ion causing the line being measured. The correction for the mass effect on emulsion sensitivity is made by dividing N by the relative sensitivity factor, $S(m)$, determined in this author's work on mass effects (see Section 4.d). The correction factor is approximately proportional to $M^{-0.5}$, where M is the mass of the ion producing the line being measured. So the corrected yield $N_{X,q}$ for ions of element X with charge q is calculated

$$N \cdot \frac{1}{q} \cdot \frac{1}{S(m)_X}$$

The concentration ratio of elements X and Y can be calculated using singly charged ions only as $C_X/C_Y = (N_{X,1}/N_{Y,1})\ (A_Y/A_X)$ where A_X and A_Y are the fractional abundances of the isotopes used for elements X and Y respectively. To correct for ion charge distribution the corrected yield, $N_{X,q}$ is determined for singly, doubly and triply charged ions, and the sum of these yields is used for the concentration calculations.

It is to be noted that the densitometer methods described above do not require the use of standard samples. These methods compare the impurity lines with matrix lines correcting for exposure ratios in the process. One advantage to this technique is that in comparing lines on the same plate, corrections are automatically made for plate to plate variations in emulsion sensitivity. A second advantage is the ability to work without standard samples. This is an important advantage in the analysis of high purity materials for which, generally, no standard samples are available. All of these methods that do not use standards suffer from a major defect in that they assume that the relative ion yield from the source is unity for all elements or that the departure from unity is known quantitatively. The validity of this assumption depends on the source, not the detector. It is mentioned here to emphasize that a correct analysis of the spectrum on the plate does not necessarily guarantee a correct analysis of the sample.

(iii) Densitometer methods with standards

There are several possible approaches that one can take in using standard samples for quantitative mass spectrography. Different approaches will give rise to different methods or, at least, modifications of a basic method. KAI AND MIKI[65] have reported three methods for use when standard samples are available. The first method requires a number of standard samples in which the impurity concentration varies over the range to be covered by the analysis. Spectra with equal exposures are made of the standard

References p. 108

samples. The optical density, D, of the lines of each impurity element is measured in all spectra and plotted against concentration, C. Spectra of the unknown samples are made with the same exposure. The impurity lines are measured and the concentrations are determined with the D *versus* C curves obtained with the standard samples. Assuming that the control is sufficient to make the sample and standard exposures under exactly the same conditions, this completely empirical method automatically corrects for all of the errors that have been discussed above. Erratic source behavior and sample inhomogeneities can still cause errors, but this is true of any method.

The second method described by KAI AND MIKI requires only one standard sample. Spectra of the standard sample are made with the exposures varying over an appreciable range. The optical density of lines of each isotope of the known impurity element in all exposures is measured. The optical density is plotted against $\log X$, where X is the product of the known concentration of the impurity times the fractional abundance of the isotope times the exposure. One exposure is made of the unknown sample, and the density of an isotope line of the element is measured. The product X is determined from the curve previously plotted, and the concentration of the impurity is calculated by dividing the product X by the exposure and by the fractional abundance of the isotope measured. This method is obviously based on the assumption that the density is a function of the product X. This is a reasonable assumption unless the matrix effects (if there are any), vary with concentration and unless the background changes markedly over the exposure range used.

The third method presented by KAI AND MIKI is for the situation in which the concentration is known in the standard sample for element A but not for element B. The density *versus* X curve is determined for element A using the second method just described above. The density of an isotope line of element B is determined in one exposure and the value of X is determined from the curve made for element A. The concentration of element B is obtained by dividing the X value just determined by the abundance of the isotope used and the exposure. This method is based on the assumption that equal concentrations of elements A and B will produce the same optical density in the same exposure. The effect of the mass difference between A and B upon the emulsion sensitivity is ignored. The method also requires that relative ion yields of the two elements at the detector is equal to the relative concentration of the elements in the sample.

As described by KAI AND MIKI none of the methods provides corrections for background or line width.

13. RELATION OF ANALYSIS OF SPECTRUM TO SAMPLE COMPOSITION

In this chapter the writer has upon occasion mentioned errors that might be caused by the ion source or by the ion beam's passage through the spectrograph. There also appears the warning that an accurate spectrum analysis does not guarantee an accurate sample analysis. This writer feels that these possibilities should be kept in mind when evaluating mass spectrographic analytical methods and results. The effects of source conditions on the energy spectra of the element reported by WOOLSTON AND HONIG [66], the great effect that variations in energy spectra can have on analytical results as reported by WOOLSTON AND HONIG [66] and by FRANZEN AND HINTENBERGER [67], and the wide spread of ionization efficiencies among the elements compel one to be cautious in stating the accuracy of the method. It appears at the time of this writing that the empirical approach such as the first method of KAI AND MIKI is by far the most reliable. This method requires standard samples, but in view of the many variables discussed in this chapter and in Chapter II, analysis without standards may contain very large errors. This is not to suggest that all such analyses contain these large errors. But it is difficult to predict the magnitude of error in an analysis without standardization, and the possibility of large errors must be considered in interpreting the results.

References p. 108

REFERENCES

1 GOLDSTEIN, *Berlin. Ber.*, 39 (1886) 691.

2 J. J. THOMSON, *Rays of Positive Electricity and Their Application to Chemical Analysis*, Longmans Green, London, 1913.

3 J. J. THOMSON, *Phil. Mag.*, 13 (1907) 561.

4 H. VON DECHEND AND W. HAMMER, *Proc. Heidelberg Acad. Sci.*, 21 (1910) 12.

5 J. KOENIGSBERGER AND J. KUTSCHEWSKI, *Physikal. Z.*, 11 (1910) 666.

6 J. J. THOMSON, *Phil. Mag.*, 21 (1911) 225.

7 J. J. THOMSON, *Rays of Positive Electricity*, 2nd ed., Longmans Green, London, 1921, p. 4.

8 J. H. WEBB, *Phys. Rev.*, 74 (1948) 511.

9 J. W. MITCHELL, *Report Prog. Phys.*, 20 (1957) 433.

10 W. H. BARKAS, *Nuclear Research Emulsions*, Vol. I, Academic Press, New York, 1963.

11 R. W. GURNEY AND N. F. MOTT, *Proc. Roy. Soc.*, A 164 (1938) 151.

12 J. W. MITCHELL, *J. Phot. Sci.*, 1 (1953) 110; *Z. Physik*, 138 (1954) 381; *Z. Elektrochem.*, 60 (1956) 557; *J. Phot. Sci.*, 5 (1957) 49; *Die photographische Empfindlichkeit*, Verlag Helvich, Darmstadt, 1957.

13 C. E. K. MEES, *The Theory of the Photographic Process*, Macmillan, New York, 1954, p. 310.

14 H. YAGODA, *Radioactive Measurements with Nuclear Emulsions*, Wiley, New York, 1949, pp. 91–93.

15 J. W. MITCHELL, *J. Phys. Chem.*, 66 (1962) 2359.

15a J. H. WEBB, *J. Opt. Soc. Am.*, 40 (1950) 3.

15b E. KLEIN, *J. Phys. Chem.*, 66 (1962) 2407.

15c P. J. VAN HEERDEN AND J. M. W. MILATZ, *Physica*, 16 (1950) 517.

16 P. BRIX, *Z. Physik.*, 126 (1949) 35.

17 J. M. MCCREA, *12th Annual Conference on Mass Spectrometry and Related Topics, Montreal, 1964.*

18 M. VON ARDENNE, *Tabellen der Elektronenphysik, Ionenphysik und Übermikroskopie*, Band I, V.e.b. Deutscher Verlag der Wissenschaften, Berlin, 1956.

18a L. MORBITZER AND A. SCHARMAN, *Z. Physik*, 181 (1964) 67.

18b H. LUTZ AND R. SIZMANN, *Z. Naturforsch.*, 19a (1964) 1079.

19 H. LICHTBLAU, *Z. Physik*, 41 (1940) 82.

20 E. BURLEFINGER AND H. EWALD, *Z. Naturforsch.*, 18a (1963) 1116.

21 P. BRIX AND H. G. DEHMELT, *Z. Physik*, 126 (1949) 728.

22 K. T. BAINBRIDGE, *J. Franklin Inst.*, 212 (1931) 489.

23 F. W. ASTON, *Mass Spectra and Isotopes*, 2nd ed., Arnold, 1941, p. 87.

24 F. W. ASTON, *Proc. Cambridge Phil. Soc.*, 22 (1925) 548.
25 J. DUCLEAUX AND P. JEANTET, *J. Phys. Radium*, 2 (1921) 154.
26 E. SCHÖNHEIT, *Naturwissenschaften*, 44 (1957) 278.
27 W. RUDLOFF, *Z. Naturforsch.*, 17a (1962) 414.
28 J. M. MCCREA, *11th Annual Conference on Mass Spectrometry and Related Topics, San Francisco, 1963.*
29 E. B. OWENS AND N. A. GIARDINO, *Anal. Chem.*, 35 (1963) 1172.
30 S. KINOSHITA, *Proc. Roy. Soc. London*, A 83 (1909) 432.
31 H. WAGNER, *Ann. Physik*, 7 (1964) 189.
32 E. BURLEFINGER AND H. EWALD, *Z. Naturforsch.*, 16a (1961) 430.
33 K. SCHWARZSCHILD, *Phot. Korr.*, 36 (1963) 109.
34 C. CANDLER, *Z. Wiss. Phot.*, 57 (1963) 199.
35 J. FRANZEN AND E. HEBEDA, *Z. Naturforsch.*, 17a (1962) 476.
36 E. DÖRNENBURG AND H. HINTENBERGER, *Z. Naturforsch.*, 16a (1961) 676.
37 M. G. INGHRAM AND R. J. HAYDEN, *A Handbook on Mass Spectroscopy*, Natl. Acad. Sci. ,Natl. Res. Council, Washington, D.C., 1954.
38 J. V. BACCOLI, JR. (Ilford Inc. New York), private communication (April 1964).
39 J. W. GUTHRIE (Sandia Corp.), *Report SC-DC-64-262*, Sandia Laboratory, Albuquerque (April 1964).
40 E. B. OWENS, *Rev. Sci. Instr.*, 32 (1961) 1420.
41 Ilford, Ltd., London, *Tech. Inform. Sheet B*, 524 (1953).
42 J. R. WOOLSTON (RCA Laboratories, Princeton), private communication (January 1964).
43 J. FRANZEN, K. H. MAURER AND K. D. SCHUY, private communication (1964).
43a P. R. KENNICOTT, *Anal. Chem.*, 37 (1965) 313.
44 H. LICHTBLAU AND J. MATTAUCH, *Z. Physik*, 117 (1941) 502.
45 J. MATTAUCH AND H. EWALD, *Naturwissenschaften*, 41 (1943) 487.
46 J. GEERK AND P. BRIX, *Z. Physik*, 125 (1949) 767.
47 W. M. HICKAM AND G. G. SWEENEY, *A.C.S. Meeting, Washington, D. C., March 1962.*
48 J. F. DUKE, in M. S. BROOKS AND J. K. KENNEDY (Editors), *Ultrapurification of Semiconductor Materials*, Macmillan, New York, 1962, p. 294.
49 J. R. CHURCHILL, *Ind. Eng. Chem., Anal. Ed.*, 16 (1944) 653.
50 C. W. HULL, *10th Mass Spectrometry Conf., New Orleans, 1962*, 404.
51 J. M. MCCREA, *15th Annual Mid-America Symposium on Spectroscopy, Chicago, 1964.*
52 H. KAWANO, *Bull. Chem. Soc. Japan*, 37 (1964) 697.
53 R. L. HEATH in J. W. GUTHRIE (Editor), *Table of Atomic Masses*, Sandia Corp., Albuquerque, 1961.

54 E. B. OWENS AND A. M. SHERMAN, Mass Spectrographic Lines of the Elements, *Tech. Report 265*, Lincoln Laboratory, M.I.T., 1962.
55 A. CORNU, R. MASSOT AND J. TERRIER, *Atlas de Raies*, Centre d'Etudes Nucleaires, Grenoble, 1963.
56 E. B. OWENS, *ASTM E-14, G.A.M.S., Brit. Inst. Pet. Conf. on Mass Spectrometry, Paris, 1964*.
57 J. FRANZEN AND H. HINTENBERGER, *Z. Naturforsch.*, 16a (1961) 535.
58 K. D. SCHUY AND H. HINTENBERGER, *Z. Naturforsch.*, 18a (1963) 926.
59 J. MATTAUCH AND R. F. K. HERZOG, *Z. Physik*, 89 (1934) 786.
60 R. D. CRAIG, G. A. ERROCK AND J. D. WALDRON, in J. D. WALDRON (Editor), *Advances in Mass Spectrometry*, Pergamon, New York, 1959, p. 145.
61 N. B. HANNAY AND A. J. AHEARN, *Anal. Chem.*, 26 (1954) 1056.
62 J. A. JAMES AND J. L. WILLIAMS, in J. D. WALDRON (Editor), *Advances in Mass Spectrometry*, Pergamon, New York, 1959.
63 G. D. PERKINS AND D. H. POLLACK, *ASD-TDR-62-275, U. S. Dept. Comm.*, 1962.
64 M. DESJARDINS, R. STEFANI, R. BOURGUILLOT AND A. CORNU, *ASTM E-14, G.A.M.S., Brit. Inst. Pet. Conf. on Mass Spectrometry, Paris, 1964*.
65 J. KAI AND M. MIKI, *Mitsub. Denki Lab. Rept.*, 5 (1964) 175.
66 J. R. WOOLSTON AND R. E. HONIG, *11th Annual Conf. on Mass Spectrometry and Related Topics, San Francisco, 1963*.
67 J. FRANZEN AND H. HINTENBERGER, *Z. Anal. Chem.*, 197 (1963) 91.

CHAPTER IV

Analysis of Special Samples*

J. W. GUTHRIE
Sandia Laboratory, Albuquerque, N. M.

1. INTRODUCTION

This chapter lists and discusses spark source mass spectrographic techniques used for analysis of: (a) liquids, (b) insulators and powders, (c) microsamples, and (d) miscellaneous samples. Emphasis is placed on techniques, and therefore only a few typical results are given. The techniques have been employed by laboratories using Mattauch–Herzog geometry double focusing instruments equipped with radio frequency, high voltage spark ion sources and photographic plate ion detectors; however, some of the techniques may be useful with other types of vacuum discharge ion sources such as the vibrating arc and the pulsed d.c. arc treated in Chapter II.

Problems concerning spark ion sources, sparking parameters, photographic plates as ion detectors, spectra identification, densitometry, plate calibrations, matrix effects, relative sensitivity factors and others have been discussed in detail in this book and elsewhere[1–10] and therefore are not in general discussed again in this chapter. The writer assumes that the reader is familiar with the spark source mass spectrographic procedures and instrumentation used for the semiquantitative analysis of trace impurities distributed homogeneously throughout the bulk of metals and semiconductors. This type of analysis has been described in many articles[11–16] and in Chapter III.

* This work was supported by the United States Atomic Energy Commission.

References p. 134

2. LIQUIDS

The analysis of impurities in liquids is similar in some respects to the analysis of surface contaminants to be discussed in the next chapter. Some liquid samples have been analyzed by contaminating the surface of an appropriate electrode with the liquid in a number of different ways. Methods of analyzing samples that are initially solutions and samples that can be made into solutions are given.

a. Electroplating and Evaporation Techniques

AHEARN[17] has demonstrated the possibilities of liquid analysis by contamination of known surfaces with impurities in liquids, using electroplating and liquid evaporation techniques for sample preparation. In the electroplating technique, clean electrodes of high purity silicon were used with low conductivity, deionized water which was doped with beryllium nitrate and arsenic oxide to give a concentration of 10^{-9} atom fraction for beryllium and for arsenic. Beryllium and arsenic were chosen for calibration purposes because in preliminary tests they were detected neither in the water, nor in the high purity silicon electrodes. The appearance of arsenic and beryllium in the electroplated silicon spectrum, along with other elements not in the silicon before electroplating, demonstrated the technique for detection of impurities at the 10^{-9} atom fraction level.

Other experiments[17] show that impurities in various liquids can be detected by simply dipping suitable electrodes into the liquid of interest and then allowing the liquid to evaporate, leaving the impurities on the electrode surfaces. To control more effectively the area on which the residue from a liquid was deposited, a novel technique was developed. Fig. 1 shows a specially shaped silicon electrode held in a pin vise and the associated electrical circuitry which will be mentioned later. Originally, the electrode was square in cross section (about 1 mm^2) throughout its length. Over a length of a few millimeters, this cross section was decreased as shown, but at the extreme tip it flared out to the original

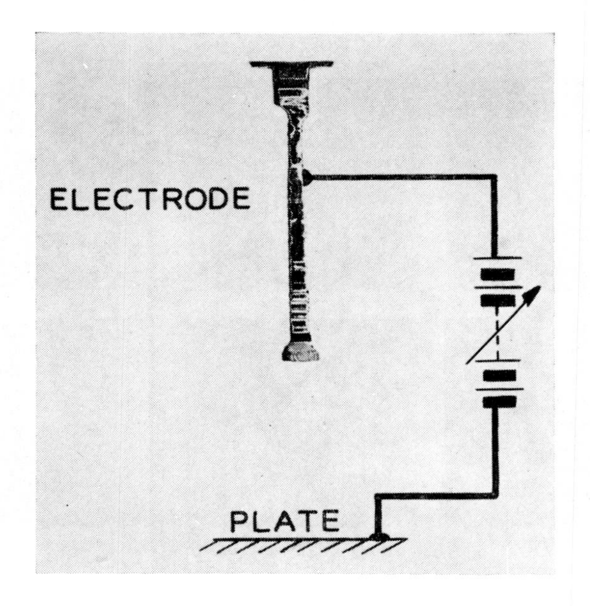

Fig. 1. Electrode tip on which water drop can be confined by electric field.

dimensions. If the mass of a drop of water is the maximum that the tip can support, the drop will hang from the electrode tip. Larger drops fall off, and smaller ones tend to creep up the electrode. By applying an electric field as indicated in Fig. 1, small drops can be pulled down toward the tip. With the flared tip end, the integrated contact force increases as the drop is pulled down; therefore, by increasing the field the drop can be pulled down on the electrode tip without pulling it off. As evaporation proceeds the remaining drop can be held at the tip by increasing the electric field, the value of which may reach several kilovolts per centimeter. The process is illustrated in Fig. 2. In (A) with zero electric field, the drop, being less than the critical mass, has crept up the electrode. By applying an appropriate electric field the drop was pulled down to the tip as shown in (B). Parts (C), (D), (E), and (F) show the remaining drop held in position by

References p. 134

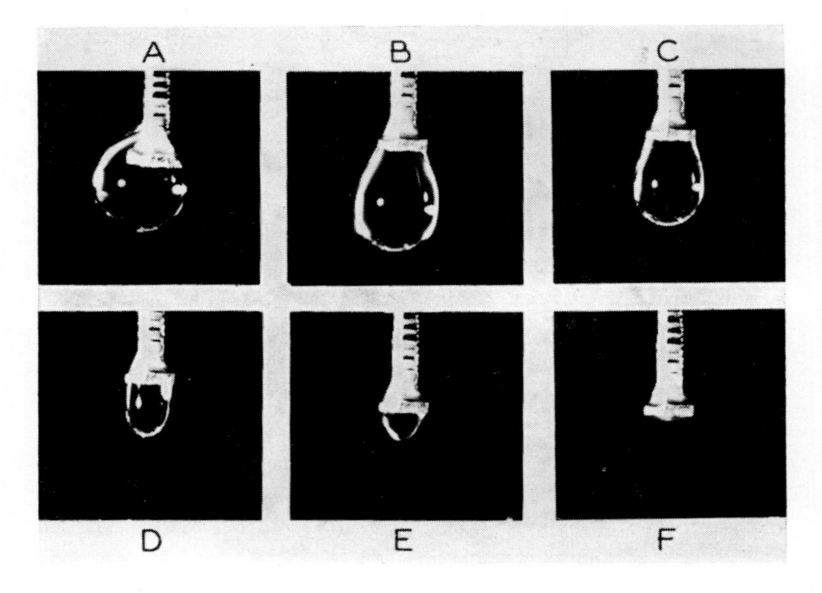

Fig. 2. Evaporation of water drop confined to electrode tip by electric field.

progressive increases in the voltage as the water evaporated. With a pointed electrode in a holder that permits adequate electrode movements during sparking, the entire surface of the coated electrode can be sampled with the spark. This technique was used to demonstrate 10^{-9} atom fraction detection with one drop of water, about 3 mm in diameter, which contained about 10^{-11} g of beryllium and about 10^{-10} g of silver.

AHEARN points out that this last technique is not limited to the case of water but should be applicable to any liquid that evaporates more rapidly than do the impurities in solution in the liquid. He suggests that analysis of body fluids, detection of nuclear fragmentation by-products in water, analysis of laboratory chemicals and petroleum products, and identification of inorganic impurities in air by dissolving in a suitable solvent should all be possible with variations of this technique.

The method of Fig. 1 was used by CHASTAGNER[18] for the elemental analysis of solids in heavy water moderator from water-moderated nuclear reactors. The concentration level of most impurities of interest was less than 100 ppb. For detection and measurement of a 1 ppb impurity in a 30 mg drop of moderator water, the bulk contamination of the electrode should be less than 1 ppm and the surface contamination should be less than 0.002 monolayer; therefore, the elimination of interfering impurities from electrodes and other materials is most important. Sparking of the electrodes in the source chamber of the mass spectrometer was found to be the most satisfactory technique for removing surface deposits on electrodes before sample loading. Silicon, indium, and gold electrodes have been used as support electrodes for samples. Transistor-grade silicon was found to be pure enough, but was unsatisfactory because the polyatomic ions mask most of the impurities being determined, including iron, cobalt, and nickel. Indium is very soft and is of limited use. Gold was found to be a reasonable compromise even though lines from iron, copper, palladium, and silver impurities are present in the spectrum.

Sparking conditions were selected such that all of the surface of the support electrode was swept completely by the spark in a single scan past the counter electrode. More than 75% of the sample deposit was removed by a scan that yielded about a $3 \cdot 10^{-9}$ C exposure.

Only small samples are analyzed because the moderator is radioactive. Since the moderator is also very pure it is impractical to add an internal standard because the unavoidable addition of impurities will almost certainly ruin the sample. Concentrations of impurity elements found in the spectrum may be calculated relative to that of an element determined by a different analytical technique. Manganese, measured by atomic absorption spectrophotometry, has been used as a reference element.

The moderator technique was also used[19] to determine elemental impurities in pond water in support of limnological investigations and in hydrochloric acid solutions in support of work on ion exchange resins.

References p. 134

b. Techniques for Organic Materials

A technique for determining trace elemental impurities at the 1 to 100 ppb level in organic and metallo-organic materials was also developed by CHASTAGNER[19]. The sample is distributed in high purity graphite as a liquid (solid samples being dissolved in appropriate solvents). A weighed portion of the organic material is slurried with a known amount of spectroscopically pure graphite powder and any solvent is evaporated. The residue is ignited in air at 800° C for 1 hour to destroy the organic material and to leave distributed in the graphite those impurities that form compounds of low volatility. Since graphite burns more slowly than organic materials, only about half the graphite is lost during ignition. The remaining graphite is pressed into rods and analyzed in the mass spectrometer. (The analysis of powders will be treated in detail in a later section.) A blank is prepared by duplicating the procedure with the solvent and graphite. The elemental impurities are determined relative to carbon, and their concentration in the original material is computed from the relative weights of graphite and sample before ignition.

A wide range of organic, organo-metallic, and organic–inorganic mixtures (such as body fluids) can be analyzed for trace elemental constituents by this method. Samples that contain volatile inorganic compounds should be treated with transistor-grade acids before ignition to reduce volatility. Samples that contain volatile metallo-organic compounds or that may react with graphite to form volatile compounds should be treated and ashed by appropriate methods such as those developed by KOIRTYOHANN AND FELDMAN[20] for the ashing of plant and animal tissue.

The quantitative aspect of the technique was evaluated by measuring the uranium and phosphorous in a uranyl nitrate organophosphorous sample dissolved in chloroform. The known weight percent of phosphorous and uranium was 8 and 30, respectively. The measured weight percents were 4 and 21. The photoplates were read visually and unit sensitivity was assumed for uranium and phosphorous.

c. *Pressed Electrode and Internal Standard Techniques*

DAVIES[21] mentions the analysis of solutions containing metallic elements using specially treated rods of very pure graphite to absorb the solution. He indicates a loss of a factor of 100 in sensitivity compared with a typical solid sample. An analysis by this technique is rapid, since only a few minutes are required to complete a plate of exposures. The method has the advantage that absolute standards may be prepared by chemical means, thereby avoiding the assumption of equal sensitivity for all elements. This is an important and unique advantage, and another example of its use will be given later. One possible disadvantage is that impurities may be differentially absorbed because of the chromatographic effects of graphite. This effect may be eliminated by using an internal standard technique such as that described by TUSHINGHAM[22]. A known quantity of a suitable standard element is dissolved in transistor-grade acid. This solution is then added to a known quantity of the liquid sample to act as an internal standard. Next, this mixture is poured onto a known quantity of pure graphite powder so that the powder is completely covered by the solution. The mixture is thoroughly stirred and then taken to dryness with continuous stirring. Finally, the dry powder is formed into electrodes using a die in a hydraulic press. Rare earths were used[23] for internal standards in the analysis of sub-microgram samples. Here the pressed electrode technique was rejected in favor of that in which the sample-internal standard solution was dried on the top of 1/8-inch diameter tantalum electrodes.

d. *Techniques for Low-Melting Point Metals*

Liquid gallium has been analyzed by several techniques. AHEARN[24] found that liquid gallium would wet the ends of clean, high purity silicon electrodes. If silicon is one of the impurities sought in the gallium analysis, then clean, high purity, germanium electrodes may be used; however, in this case it was necessary to supersonically agitate the electrode to make the gallium wet the

References p. 134

germanium. BROWN *et al.*[25] have analyzed gallium by supporting it on the ends of high purity graphite electrodes. WOLSTENHOLME[26] describes a method for the analysis of gallium which uses liquid nitrogen to chill copper strips attached to the electrode clamps. Thus the electrodes are self-supporting. He found that this technique was also an improvement, with respect to selective distillation of impurities, over the method of supporting liquid gallium on graphite electrodes. FITZNER[27] has also used the chilling technique for analysis of gallium and found silver strips more effective than copper. He points out that the chilled gallium is very fragile and that contact between chilled electrodes should be avoided. The electrode chilling technique was used by NALBANTOGLU[28] for the analysis of gallium and mercury.

e. Use of Standard Solutions

Standard solutions can sometimes be used to simulate the sample in the analysis of liquid samples. A recent experiment in the writer's laboratory will serve as an example. It was desired to measure the ratio of aluminum to titanium in a dilute solution of ammonium bifluoride. The total solution volume available was of the order of 0.02 cc. It was decided that a technique of evaporating the sample solution on a supporting electrode would be tried.

The first step was to find an electrode material whose surface was free of aluminum and titanium, or one from which these contaminants could be easily removed and whose spectrum did not interfere with the elements of interest. A flattened copper wire bent in an L shape and etched in nitric acid was found to meet the requirements for a sample support electrode.

A preliminary sample analysis indicated that the Al/Ti ratio was such that both the Al and Ti spectra from a single exposure could be used to obtain analytical data. If the ratio had been much different, it would have been necessary to add an internal standard element to different portions of the sample solution, use one or more exposures on the plate to determine the Al/internal standard element ratio and a different spiked sample portion and exposures to measure the Ti/internal standard element ratio, and then obtain the Al/Ti ratio from the sets of data.

One standard solution containing known amounts of titanium, aluminum, and ammonium bifluoride was prepared. The concentration of ammonium bifluoride in the sample solution was known approximately. The ammonium bifluoride and other solutions used to make the standard solution were analyzed for aluminum and titanium contamination, but none was found. About $4 \cdot 10^{-6}$ liters of standard solution containing about $4 \cdot 10^{-8}$ g of aluminum and about $36 \cdot 10^{-8}$ g of titanium was pipetted onto a 2 by 4 mm area of the flattened L-shaped copper wire. The Al/Ti ratio approximated that initially estimated from the preliminary sample analysis. After drying the standard sample, the electrode was mounted in the mass spectrometer and a pointed copper counter electrode was used to scan the standard sample deposit area of the support electrode during sparking.

The quantity of material deposited was usually sufficient for two to four separate exposures which yielded densitometer data in the desirable linear portion of the plate calibration curve that yielded relative intensity values for aluminum and titanium and thus the Al/Ti ratio. The counter electrode was moved about the entire sample deposit area during each exposure. Two sets of electrodes of the standard, and at least two sets of electrodes of the sample, prepared and sparked in a similar fashion, were recorded on each plate.

About fifty analyses of the standard solution, on several plates also containing spectra of several similar samples, gave encouraging results. The results of the standard sample analyses provided confidence in the sample results, in the technique for plate calibration,[29] and in various correction factors, including the correction for plate response differences for ions of different mass and the correction for line width differences[1] used in computations for this particular sample. No correction was made for any differences in the relative sensitivity coefficient of aluminum and titanium. This is perhaps the simplest use of a standard solution,

References p. 134

but the advantage of preparing standards by chemical means was evident.

Mention was made above that one sample loading of the Ti–Al–ammonium bifluoride solution sometimes provided two to four separate exposures each producing about the same calculated Al/Ti ratio. The situation was different for similar analyses of cadmium to erbium ratios in hydrochloric acid solutions using copper and also gold for support and counter electrodes. Only one calculation of the Cd/Er ratio was possible from one sample loading because experiments showed that cadmium was leaving the electrode at a greater rate than erbium. Therefore, two methods were used to obtain correct ratios as determined by analysis of standard mixtures like that described above. In the first method, all of the sample was removed and recorded in one spectrum (verified by a separate exposure). In the second method, the ion yields[1] for Er^+ and Cd^+ were summed from all separate exposures made during scans of the entire sample area. For the samples of interest and depending on the length of individual exposures for the second method, the cadmium spectrum was usually recorded only in the first exposure while the erbium spectrum was recorded in more than one exposure. Each exposure was made from an entire scan of the sample-containing area of the support electrode. The beam monitor was not used to control exposures because its output had an unknown relationship with the sample ions. Final exposures should show only the spectrum of the electrode materials, indicating that all the sample available had been sparked off.

The method described has also been useful in measuring ratios of two or more materials which have been deposited as thin film layers on various substrates. By dissolving the thin film layers, a homogeneous mixture is available for analysis of elemental ratios; however, no figure of distribution of a given element on the original substrate is available if all the film is initially removed. If ratios only are required, then the exact volumes of solution used do not necessarily have to be controlled. Concentrations of elements instead of ratios of elements in the solution can be determined by various techniques if required, and in this case the volumes of solution used may be important. One disadvantage of the method is that for good results the evaporated solution should leave only a thin layer of residue on the electrode. If this is not the case, then the residue scab may be physically knocked off the electrode in gross unionized quantities during sparking, and poor results can be expected. For sample solutions that leave heavy residues of unwanted material upon evaporation, a different technique involving the mixing of sample with graphite (or other material) and pressing into electrodes will produce more satisfactory results. (This mixing and pressing technique will be discussed in more detail in the section on Insulators and Powders.)

Ratios of the major elemental materials in thin films deposited as layers on various substrates may also be determined by sparking the sample directly if care is taken to spark off all the film in a given area and assuming the film is not so thin as to require an unreasonable area to be sparked in order to obtain required exposures. Of course, this care is not required if ratios are needed for elemental materials in a homogeneous film. Limited quantities of thin film material can seriously restrict the concentration or ratio level of impurities that may be detected either by sparking directly to a film on a substrate or using a solution method.

3. INSULATORS AND POWDERS

In early work (*e.g.* refs. 11, 12, 24, 30, 31) with powders and insulators including organic compounds[23,32,33], the sample was packed or wrapped in metal tubes, cups, or foil and then used as electrodes. It was hoped that the spark would sample the powder or insulator simultaneously with the conductor. JENSEN *et al.*[34] use the "powder-in-cup technique" to analyze solids formed in rocket propellant combustion processes. GOSHGARIAN[35] uses a unique method for handling samples such as $LiAlH_4$ and $NaBH_4$ which are reactive with air or moisture. The samples are loaded into cupped electrodes inside a dry box in an inert atmosphere and then each electrode with its sample is covered

References p. 134

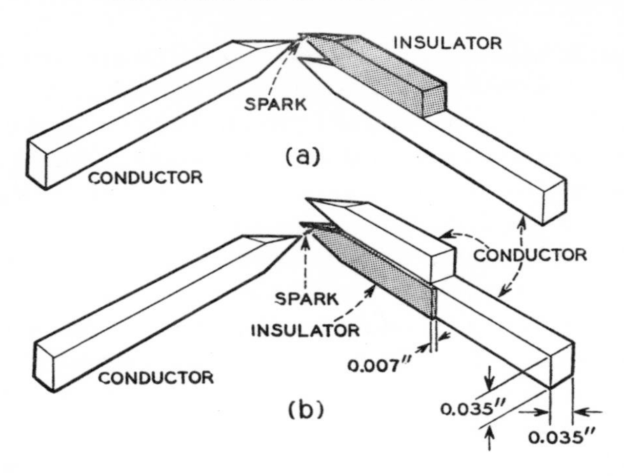

Fig. 3. Technique of AHEARN[30] for ionizing nonconducting samples.

with teflon or polyethylene film (held on the 1/8-inch cupped electrode with a 1/8-inch teflon sleeve) for transfer to the spark source chamber of the mass spectrometer. After the spark source chamber is evacuated, the film is removed by manipulation of the probe electrode. BROWN *et al.*[16] analyzed Raney nickel by applying a wet paste of the sample to the end of a graphite electrode. Other techniques used were to physically press sample powder into the end of a graphite electrode[36] or to sinter suitable powder samples[30]. Nonconducting solids in a more massive state have been analyzed successfully by mounting suitable shapes of the sample material in close conjunction with conducting electrodes to be sampled during the sparking process[16,30,36]. Fig. 3 (a and b) shows a method used by AHEARN[30]. When the conductor electrode is brought near the insulator with the usual spark voltage applied (about 50 kV), a vacuum spark is produced between the two. The mass spectrum is a mixture of the conductor and the insulator. By means of electrode positioners a spark can also be formed between the two conductors in order to obtain the spectrum of the conductor alone together with the background characteristic of the instrument. The difference between these spectra yields the

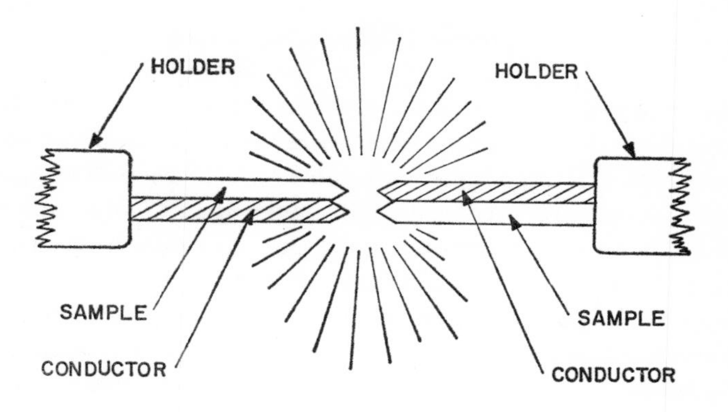

Fig. 4. Technique of JAMES AND WILLIAMS [36] for ionizing nonconducting samples.

spectrum of the insulator. Fig. 4 shows another method used by JAMES AND WILLIAMS[36]. An auxiliary electrode of pure graphite is put in each electrode clamp beside the sample electrode. The radio frequency spark is initiated between the auxiliary electrodes and, by varying the relative positions of the electrodes, the relative amounts of sample and auxiliary electrodes being ionized can be varied. The main component (silicon in this case) of the insulator's ion current was monitored electronically after mass separation at the high radius portion of the magnetic field. This allowed only impurities of lower mass than silicon to be recorded on the photographic plate; thus, this technique has definite limitations. To overcome this difficulty, OWENS[37] has used a device which allows the electrometer ion detector to be placed at any mass position desired while still covering with the photographic plate the rest of the mass spectrum between mass 6 and mass 250. Another technique for obtaining the spectrum of an insulator is to deposit a strip of metal, *e.g.*, gold, on the insulator and then spark near the gold-insulator junction with a pointed gold counter electrode.

References p. 134

a. Pressed Electrode Techniques

The greatest drawback to most of the techniques mentioned above is that the ratio of sample to supporting material being ionized is erratic and it is practically impossible to use the beam monitor to control the exposures relative to sample ions. To overcome this drawback, several laboratories are using the method reported by ERROCK[38] in 1962, or variations of that method. In general, powdered samples (obtained by grinding or otherwise converting solid bulk insulators into powders) are mixed with various amounts of graphite or suitable metal powders and then pressed into a mold to form electrodes. Ideal electrodes would be about 1 cm long and about 2 mm in diameter. Sample electrodes formed by this pressed electrode technique usually give spectra in which the ratio of sample to conducting powder material is constant. Therefore, the beam monitor can be used to control sample exposure. Concentration of impurity elements may be calculated relative to a major matrix element of the sample or relative to the supporting material element. For the latter choice, the ratio of supporting material element to sample is usually known. For some samples, a liquid technique or a combination liquid–powder technique (see previous section on liquids) may also be used.

Five requirements listed by BROWN AND WOLSTENHOLME[39] for pressed sample electrodes to permit the successful analysis of insulating powders are: (a) the electrodes must be electrically conducting; (b) the physical strength must be sufficient so that the electrodes can be clamped in the electrode holders; (c) there must be minimum interference from the mass spectrum of the support material; (d) any impurities in the support material must be present at low and known concentrations; and (e) for quantitative analysis, the contribution of the support material (and the sample) to the spark and, therefore, to the total ion current, should be constant and consistent. Certain grades of graphite have been found to meet the requirements listed. The pressed electrode method has been successfully applied[39] to the quantitative analysis of a variety of samples including powdered rocks of geological interest, aluminum oxide, titanium dioxide, thorium dioxide, magnesium oxide, bauxite, sodium azide, cadmium sulfide and others. For a typical example, Table I shows results obtained for the analysis of three thorium dioxide samples. To remove any surface contamination from the pressed sample rod, BROWN AND WOLSTENHOLME[39] scrape the rod, then break it in the middle to obtain two electrodes. They suggest mixing graphite and sample powder in about equal amounts. TUSHINGHAM[22] has mixed graphite

TABLE I
ANALYSIS OF THREE THORIUM DIOXIDE SAMPLES
(BROWN AND WOLSTENHOLME[39])

Elements detected (ppm atomic)			
Element	1	2	3
Bismuth	0.03	1	< 0.03
Lead	0.6	0.3	6
Tantalum	1	0.3	20
Samarium	30	50	7
Neodymium	100	160	16
Praseodymium	50	30	3
Cerium	1,000	300	20
Lanthanum	40	20	10
Barium	2	1,400	2
Niobium	1	30	0.1
Zirconium	20	200	20
Strontium	2	50	1
Zinc	6	20	2
Copper	10	30	1
Nickel	40	40	4
Cobalt	3	300	3
Iron	400	400	80
Manganese	3	10	1
Titanium	40	4,000	20
Sulfur	500	4,000	100
Phosphorus	100	20	5,000
Silicon	1,200	20,000	1,200

References p. 134

with conducting powders in order to press into electrodes those samples that will not themselves compact into electrodes. He prefers samples as fine as flour for mixing with graphite. BLOSSER[23] suggests a 15- to 30-minute grinding and/or mixing for successful analysis.

The pressed electrode technique, with graphite as the support material, was used by WOLSTENHOLME[40] to analyze blood plasma. The technique was applied to the dried blood plasma directly and also after ignition of a known weight of the sample. The graphite support matrix was analyzed separately. Elemental concentrations

TABLE II

ANALYSIS OF DRIED BLOOD PLASMA

Element	Mass spectrometry (WOLSTENHOLME[40]) ppm weight	Typical average values (BOWEN[41]) ppm weight
Lead*	0.2	0.7
Iodine	1.0	1.4
Strontium*	0.7	0.56
Rubidium	14.0	34.0
Bromine	50.0	150.0
Zinc*	12.0	31.0
Copper	26.0	19.0
Iron	400	20.0
Manganese*	2	0.06
Chromium*	5	0.4
Potassium	25,000	2,740
Chlorine	17,000	62,000
Sulfur**	5,400	14,600
Phosphorus	2,000	1,900
Aluminum*	5	7.0
Magnesium	500	374
Sodium	--- Major component ---	
Fluorine*	6	4.8

* Not detected in unignited sample. Value quoted is for ignited sample.
** From unignited sample.

were estimated by the visual method of CRAIG, ERROCK AND WALDRON[13] which assumes that all elements have the same sensitivity. In Table II, results for elements detected by mass spectrometry are compared with the average values published by the UK Atomic Energy Authority for typical blood plasma samples[41]. Additional elements were detected by mass spectrometry, and limits of detection for 46 elements not detected are given[40]. The mass spectrometer results for most elements agree within about a factor of three with those of the "typical" results. This degree of agreement is reasonable for the technique used[13]. Results for potassium, chromium, manganese, and iron show a wider discrepancy. The high value for potassium may be due to thermal ionization effects and a high relative sensitivity factor. The discrepancies for chromium and manganese were unexplained, but contamination is a possibility. The particular blood sample analyzed was rejected from stock because of an abnormally high iron content.

As mentioned previously, substances other than graphite have been used for supporting material. REUTER AND KUPTSIS[42] report that powders of conducting or nonconducting materials were successfully analyzed after the preparation of pressed bars containing an intimate mixture of silver powder and sample. Bars of good mechanical resistance were obtained with pressures of about 20,000 psi and mixtures containing 3 weight parts of silver and 1 weight part of the sample. This technique was used for the analysis of rare earth impurities in rare earth compounds. For elements other than the rare earths in the rare earth compounds, pressed bars of the intimate mixture of graphite and sample were used.

Detailed studies of the pressed electrode technique have been made by OWENS[37] who has used the technique principally for nonconductors but has also used it for conductors and semiconductors that are received as powder and for any sample that is too small to use directly as a self electrode. Demonstration that exposures relative to the sample can be monitored with the total ion beam monitor was made by testing the constancy of the ratio

References p. 134

of sample ions to support material ions in recorded spectra. This was done with electrodes made by pressing a mixture of powdered ruby and powdered graphite (both fine enough to pass through a 100-mesh sieve) and then measuring the aluminum-to-carbon ratio in many separate exposures of the sparked electrodes. In twelve exposures, the aluminum-to-carbon ratio showed a relative standard deviation of 17%. For further evidence, spectra of 33 different samples run by the pressed electrode technique were examined. Results were similar to those already mentioned.

The powdering of samples without introducing impurities was studied[37]. The very hard samples such as rubies, are powdered in a hard steel mortar and pestle. Most of the hard sample materials are relatively inert chemically, and the steel that is ground up with the sample material can be dissolved in suitable high purity acids and washed away with distilled water. Less hard and less inert materials are ground by placing chips of the material in a plastic vial with a plastic ball and shaking in the Wig-L-Bug* shaker. Since plastic will be ground with the material, plastics containing inorganic fillers or impurities should not be used. With reasonable resolution in the spectra, the carbon and hydrocarbon lines from the plastic can be separated and identified from the ion lines of the inorganic materials.

The choice of conducting powder is limited due to the difficulty of obtaining pure materials. OWENS has tried Ag, Ti, Sn, Ni and Cu, but silver is the only metal powder found available with sufficient purity for pressed electrode work. However, the producer of the particular silver powder has not been able to maintain a consistent high level of purity in all batches of powder, and much of the silver powder purchased has been discarded because of high impurity levels. Graphite is the conductor powder that is most generally used and it is available at a consistently high level of purity.

There are several disadvantages in using graphite as the conducting powder[37]. The electrodes are not as strong as those made

* A patented, commercially available, electric mortar.

from metal powders. A higher sample-to-conducting powder ion ratio can be obtained in electrodes made with metal powders than those made with graphite. A pressed electrode with sufficient strength can be made with a 2 to 1 ratio by weight of Ag to SnO_2 (3 to 1 mole ratio). It was found that it requires at least a 3 to 1 ratio by weight of graphite to SnO_2 (about 37 to 1 mole ratio) to obtain an electrode with sufficient strength to hold together while being placed in the electrode clamps and while the exposures are being made. Thus, to obtain equal exposures relative to the SnO_2 sample, the exposure measured by the total ion beam monitor must be about 12 times greater for the graphite–SnO_2 electrodes than for the Ag–SnO_2 electrodes. In addition, the impurities in the graphite must be a factor of 12 lower than in the silver to maintain equal analytical sensitivity. With graphite, there is the tendency for many elements to form carbides. The rare earths are especially troublesome in this respect. The rare earth carbide formation is appreciable, and the extra spectral lines of the carbides add greatly to the difficulty of interpreting the overlapping isotope patterns of these elements. Because of the disadvantages in using graphite as the conducting powder, metal powders are preferred if they can be obtained with the necessary purity.

A variation of the pressed electrode technique has been used by ADDINK[43] AND HARVEY[33] who have analyzed insulating powders by pressing together the powder to be analyzed and a thin backing layer of graphite. Using this method, they state that the contribution of the graphite powder and its impurities are diminished by about a factor of 10, compared with spectra obtained by sparking pressed mixtures of the powder to be analyzed and graphite. Other possibilities include the work being done by HARVEY[33] in a laser crystal program with several promising "backing" techniques which may render the powdering of a sample unnecessary.

References p. 134

4. MICROSAMPLES

Microsample techniques discussed here will be limited to those concerning isolated particles of small mass, *e.g.*, tiny crystals, whiskers, filings, etc. Microprobe techniques for sampling singularities in large bodies, such as inclusions or segregations at grain boundaries or other localized inhomogeneities, are discussed in the following chapter.

The success in analyzing microsamples depends largely upon finding a satisfactory method to mount the specimen in or on a supporting electrode and the ability to confine the spark to the item of interest. Various materials such as graphite, indium, and silicon have been used as supports for small samples. A sharp pointed probe electrode is usually used to spark to the sample, sometimes with the aid of a microscope to view the procedure. Some types of microsamples may be analyzed by techniques already discussed in the previous sections on liquids and powders.

a. Sample Support Techniques

Small silicon crystals were analyzed by AHEARN[24] by mounting a crystal between two pieces of previously analyzed silicon. JAMES AND WILLIAMS[36] used a slotted piece of graphite to hold a single cat's whisker from a radar diode. Individual crystals of cadmium sulfide for photocells have also been examined by this technique[14]. Indium electrodes were used by FITZSIMMONS *et al.*[44] to support 2 mg crystals of natural graphite. Indium was chosen because high purity quantities are available, it is very malleable, and its two isotopes have odd mass numbers; therefore, the multiply charged indium ions have less chance of interfering with lower mass, singly charged ions of other elements. Others[23, 42, 45, 46] have also used indium for support electrodes. Small diameter (0.0015 inch) copper wires have been analyzed by DAVIES[47] by twisting the wires into bundles and supporting the bundles in the spark source electrode clamps with compacted graphite rods. This is one way to eliminate the melting-together problem when attempts are made to spark directly between two small diameter wires. Another way is to spark between a plane surface and the small wire.

A simple but unique technique for supporting small crystals is used by HICKAM[48]. The sample is sandwiched between two high purity gold foils using a press. This process embeds the crystals in the gold and provides suitable support. The sandwich is then torn apart, and one has two uncontaminated samples mounted on the gold foil. Silicon carbide crystals have been embedded in gold for analysis by this technique. A pointed, gold wire counter electrode can be used to scan the sample area. The crystals are sampled during the spark process between the gold foil support electrode and the counter electrode. A different technique for the analysis of small irregularly shaped crystallites is used by REUTER AND KUPTSIS[42]. Their technique is to mount the sample on a high purity support electrode with the aid of silver epoxy (1 part silver, and 2 parts paste). No problem is reported in obtaining normal low pressures in the spark source chamber. The contribution of the silver to the sample spectrum due to stray sparking is normally less than 5 ppm, and the hydrocarbon background is of the same order as observed with the support electrodes in the absence of epoxy. In the writer's laboratory, a qualitative analysis was made to determine the major elemental materials (considered proprietary by the supplier) in five different components of miniature rectifier assemblies. A sharp needle made of high purity gold was used for the probe electrode to spark to the areas of interest.

5. MISCELLANEOUS SAMPLES

a. Gas Analysis

Few results have been reported for the analysis of bulk quantities of carbon, hydrogen, nitrogen, and oxygen in metal samples, even though atomic ions of these elements are recorded in the metal sample spectrum with other impurities (with the possible exception

References p. 134

of H^+ ions which, to be recorded, require a lower magnet current setting than is normally used). The elements mentioned above make up the residual gases usually found in vacuum systems, and if these residual gases become involved in the sparking process of various electrode materials, they may make contributions to the recorded spectrum. Since samples with considerable gas content may cause noticeable pressure increases in the spark source chamber during sparking, it is possible that the gaseous materials may participate in the spark process more than once before they are finally pumped away[16]. The intensity of the gaseous species recorded seems to be dependent somewhat on sparking parameters. The writer has observed that the O^+ line recorded during constant exposures (beam monitor readings) with copper electrodes, for example, was noticeably more intense at low spark repetition rates than at high rates. If reliable standard samples were available with known low gas contents, background contribution could perhaps be evaluated.

The analysis of oxygen in beryllium is more successfully done according to BLOSSER[23] when the spark is not turned off between successive exposures in order to minimize gettering by the sample. He always pre-sparks samples and then makes the exposures from heavy to light when looking for gases and if surface contaminants are of no interest. A source bake is considered essential, although he states that in several experiments fair results were obtained when the sample was scraped and loaded under helium into a previously baked source chamber. ROBOZ[49] has reported on experiments which showed that the nitrogen content of iron and titanium samples with known gas concentrations could be determined with essentially the same accuracy and precision as those for other elements. National Bureau of Standards steel and titanium samples containing nitrogen in the 100 to 600 ppm atomic range were used in the experiments. In order to determine a value for nitrogen background in the mass spectrometer, several high purity materials were analyzed. The lowest value—10 ppm—observed was with a high purity silver sample. Therefore the nitrogen background was considered to be insignificant in the steel and titanium analyses. GUTHRIE[50, 51] found a lack of agreement between analysis of carbon, hydrogen, nitrogen, and oxygen in erbium metal by spark mass spectrometry, neutron activation (used for nitrogen and oxygen), and microcombustion (used for hydrogen and carbon) techniques. Values obtained by spark mass spectrometry were usually considerably lower than the values obtained by the two other techniques for the particular samples mentioned.

b. Isotopic Analysis

The technique of isotopic dilution gives one of the most accurate and sensitive analyses that can be made on a mass spectrometer. To test the method with the spark source instrument, LEIPZIGER[52] chose to analyze a sample for copper. Copper, titanium, platinum, and cadmium are examples of elements which are not readily ionized by normal surface or electron impact ionization techniques, nor is copper commonly associated with stable isotope dilution techniques. A National Bureau of Standards nickel oxide powder which had an average copper value of 20 ppm was chosen for the test. LEIPZIGER's procedure involved weighing a 1-gram sample, micropipetting a known amount of ^{65}Cu spike, and dissolving the sample. The copper was concentrated by electrolysis, redissolved, and then coated on pure aluminum electrodes for sparking in the usual manner. The copper isotopic ratio was obtained from the calibrated plate (tin exposures on the same plate were used for plate calibration), and the copper content was calculated by the usual methods for isotopic dilution work. The average copper value for six analyses was 21 ppm with a S.D. of 1.3. LEIPZIGER AND CROFT[52, 53] have also made successful geologic age determinations by direct lead isotope analysis on samples cut from massive specimens, thus avoiding several manipulations common with other analytical methods.

References p. 134

6. CONCLUSIONS

From the techniques discussed in this chapter it should be evident that the spark source mass spectrograph has considerable potential value for producing useful results in the analysis of liquids, insulators and powders, microsamples, and miscellaneous samples. Analysis of "special samples" has already made considerable contribution to the over-all usefulness of a spark source mass spectrograph in several laboratories.

There is no other single analytical technique that can so quickly and conveniently produce such a full analysis with such advantages as high sensitivity, approximate equality of sensitivity for all elements, simplicity of interpretation, over-all coverage of the elements in a single analysis, ease of adaptation to new problems and little need for reference standards for many samples. There is certainly a very real possibility that as more understanding and experience are gained in all areas of spark source mass spectroscopy, and as the techniques described in this chapter become more refined, they should effectively complement other methods of survey analysis.

REFERENCES

1 E. B. Owens and N. A. Giardino, *Anal. Chem.*, 35 (1963) 1172.
2 E. B. Owens, *ASTM E-14 Meeting on Mass Spectrometry, Montreal, 1964*, Paper No. 40.
3 R. E. Honig, *ASTM E-14 Meeting on Mass Spectrometry, Montreal, 1964*, Paper No. 38.
4 J. Franzen, K. D. Schuy and H. Hintenberger, *ASTM E-14 Meeting on Mass Spectrometry, Montreal, 1964*, Paper No. 39.
5 J. R. Woolston and R. E. Honig, *ASTM E-14 Meeting on Mass Spectrometry, San Francisco, 1963*, Paper No. 106.
6 J. R. Woolston and R. E. Honig, *ASTM E-14 Meeting on Mass Spectrometry, Montreal, 1964*, Paper No. 57.
7 J. M. McCrea, *ASTM E-14 Meeting on Mass Spectrometry, Montreal, 1964*, Paper No. 92.
8 J. S. Halliday, A. Harrison and A. Riddoch, *ASTM E-14 Meeting on Mass Spectrometry, Montreal, 1964*, Paper No. 56.

9 C. M. JUDSON AND C. W. HULL, *ASTM E-14 Meeting on Mass Spectrometry, San Francisco, 1963*, Paper No. 83.
10 W. REUTER AND J. D. KUPTSIS, *Third National Meeting of the Society for Applied Spectroscopy, Cleveland, 1964*, Paper No. 53.
11 N. B. HANNAY AND A. J. AHEARN, *Anal. Chem.*, 26 (1954) 1056.
12 N. B. HANNAY, *Science*, 134 (1961) 1220.
13 R. D. CRAIG, G. A. ERROCK AND J. D. WALDRON, in J. D. WALDRON (Editor), *Advances in Mass Spectrometry*, Vol. 1, Pergamon, Oxford, 1959.
14 R. BROWN, R. D. CRAIG, J. A. JAMES AND C. M. WILSON, in M. S. BROOKS AND J. K. KENNEDY (Editors), *Ultrapurification of Semiconductor Materials*, Macmillan, New York, 1962, p. 279.
15 J. F. DUKE, in M. S. BROOKS AND J. K. KENNEDY (Editors), *Ultrapurification of Semiconductor Materials*, Macmillan, New York, 1962, p. 294.
16 R. BROWN, R. D. CRAIG AND R. M. ELLIOTT, in R. M. ELLIOTT (Editor), *Advances in Mass Spectrometry*, Vol. 2, Pergamon, Oxford, 1962.
17 A. J. AHEARN, *J. Appl. Phys.*, 32 (1961) 1197.
18 P. CHASTAGNER, *ASTM E-14 Meeting on Mass Spectrometry, Montreal, 1964*, Paper No. 55.
19 P. CHASTAGNER, *Appl. Spectry.*, 19 (1965) 33.
20 S. R. KOIRTYOHANN AND C. FELDMAN, *Anal. Chem. Div. Annual Report for period ending 12-31-63, ORNL 3397*, (1963) 62.
21 T. A. DAVIES, in P. W. WEST (Editor), *Analytical Chemistry 1962*, Elsevier, Amsterdam, 1963.
22 R. TUSHINGHAM, United Kingdom Atomic Energy Authority, Capenhurst Works, private communication, July 1964.
23 E. R. BLOSSER, Battelle Memorial Institute, private communication, August 1964.
24 A. J. AHEARN, *ASTM E-14 Meeting on Mass Spectrometry, San Francisco, 1963*, Paper No. 42.
25 R. BROWN, R. D. CRAIG, J. A. JAMES AND C. M. WILSON, *Conference on Ultrapurification of Semiconductor Materials, Boston, April 1961.*
26 W. A. WOLSTENHOLME, *Appl. Spectry*, 17 (1963) 51.
27 E. FITZNER, Swiss Aluminum Ltd., private communication, July 1964.
28 M. NALBANTOGLU, Analysis of Metals with Low Melting Points by Spark Source Mass Spectroscopy, *ASTM E-14, G.A.M.S. Brit. Inst. Pet. Meeting, Paris, September 1964.*
29 J. W. GUTHRIE, *Sandia Laboratory Report SC-TM-64-534*, Sandia Laboratory, Albuquerque, April 1964.
30 A. J. AHEARN, *J. Appl. Phys.*, 32 (1961) 1195.

31 J. M. McCrea, U.S. Steel, Applied Physics Laboratory, private communication, July 1964.
32 M. Desjardins, F. N. Hodgson and W. Baun, *ASTM E-14 Meeting on Mass Spectrometry, New Orleans, 1962*, Paper No. 20.
33 L. Harvey, Admiralty Materials Laboratory, private communication, September 1964.
34 A. V. Jensen, B. B. Goshgarian and N. E. Dane, *ASTM E-14 Meeting on Mass Spectrometry, San Francisco, 1963*, Paper No. 100.
35 B. B. Goshgarian, Air Force Rocket Propulsion Laboratory, Edwards, Calif., private communication, August 1964.
36 J. A. James and J. L. Williams, in J. D. Waldron (Editor), *Advances in Mass Spectrometry*, Vol. 1, Pergamon, Oxford, 1959.
37 E. B. Owens, The Mass Spectrographic Analysis of Powdered Samples, *Presented at ASTM E-14, G.A.M.S. Brit. Inst. Pet. Meeting, Paris, September 1964.*
38 G. A. Errock, *Xth International Conference on Spectroscopy, College Park, Md., June 1962.*
39 R. Brown and W. A. Wolstenholme, *ASTM E-14 Meeting on Mass Spectrometry, San Francisco, 1963*, Paper No. 75; *Nature*, 201 (1964) 598.
40 W. A. Wolstenholme, *Nature*, 203 (1964) 1284.
41 H. J. M. Bowen, *U.K. At. Energy Authority Rept. No. R.4196.*
42 W. Reuter and J. D. Kuptsis, IBM T. J. Watson Research Center, private communication, October 1964.
43 N. W. H. Addink, Philips Research Laboratories, Eindhoven, private communication, July 1964.
44 R. G. Fitzsimmons, W. Fletcher and R. Tushingham, *ASTM E-14 Meeting on Mass Spectrometry, New Orleans, 1962*, Paper No. 74.
45 A. J. Socha and R. K. Willardson, *ASTM E-14 Meeting on Mass Spectrometry, San Francisco, 1963*, Paper No. 84.
46 R. Craig and W. A. Wolstenholme, Determination of Impurities in Solids by Mass Spectrometry, *Presented at the Chemical Society Conference in Belgium, October 1963.*
47 R. L. Davies, British Insulated Callendars' Cables Ltd., private communication, July 1964.
48 W. M. Hickam, Westinghouse Research and Development Center, private communication, September 1961.
49 J. Roboz, *ASTM E-14 Meeting on Mass Spectrometry, San Francisco, 1963*, Paper No. 103.
50 J. W. Guthrie, *ASTM E-14 Meeting on Mass Spectrometry, Montreal, 1964*, Paper No. 54.
51 J. W. Guthrie, *J. Less-Common Metals*, 7 (1964) 420.

52 F. D. Leipziger, *ASTM E-14 Meeting on Mass Spectrometry, San Francisco, 1963*, Paper No. 97.
53 F. D. Leipziger and W. J. Croft, *Geochim. Cosmochim. Acta*, 28 (1964) 268.

CHAPTER V

Mass Spectrographic Microprobe Analysis

W. M. HICKAM AND G. G. SWEENEY
Westinghouse Research Laboratories, Pittsburgh, Pa. 15235

1. INTRODUCTION

The frequent need for obtaining the composition of micro-quantities of solid material has brought about the modification of many techniques and the development of new techniques for microanalyses. Throughout the development of analytical mass spectrometers, the users have been restricted to the analysis of small quantities of materials because most of the systems are incapable of handling large quantities. Numerous types of ion sources have been used for studying microquantities of solids and a number of these have been considered within a probe concept. These include vaporization followed by electron impact ionization[1,2], thermal ionization[3], ion bombardment[4,5], laser[6], and vacuum spark[7]. The author of Chapter II discusses in detail the functioning of these and other mass spectrometric ion sources reported for the excitation of solids. In this chapter the authors will explore the subject of the use of the radio-frequency spark source mass spectrograph within a microprobe concept for inorganics and its extention to organics. Although the activity on this subject has been rather limited to date, it is hoped that the examples presented will suffice to illustrate the potential usefulness of this approach and thus stimulate others.

Numerous parameters associated with the operation of the spark source mass spectrograph suggest the usefulness of this technique for the analysis of microsamples. These parameters include a sensitivity of the order of 10^{11} atoms for most of the elements, a linear response with concentration, and a simple identification and interpretation scheme. The early work of DEMPSTER[8], GORMAN, JONES AND HIPPLE[9], and HANNAY AND AHEARN[10], and numerous later works in this field confirm that such conclusions are correct at least semi-quantitatively.

The vacuum radio frequency spark source mass spectrograph, as it is used today to obtain elemental composition of solids, implies an ionic representation of a solid resulting from repetitive sampling events, repetitive ion generating events, repetitive ion transmission and separation events, and repetitive recording events. It is extremely difficult to establish if the entire system is repetitive and additive starting at time zero, as defined by the initiation of the spark. Many parameters undergo severe change at time zero on the electrode surfaces: in fact time zero may be difficult to define. For example, using thin beryllium windows and counters, X-ray emission is observed with no visible spark for extended periods of time after applying a 30–50 kV radio frequency supply to a point-to-plane configuration. The numerous parameters that make zero time difficult to define and the rapid changes occurring shortly thereafter complicate the interpretation of spectra achieved within short time intervals after zero time. In the use of the instrument as a microprobe, it is important to develop a better understanding of events occurring on initiation of the spark and shortly thereafter.

Mass spectrographic microprobe analysis implies that the composition of specified small volumes of various geometries is obtained. In practice, the magnitude of the linear dimensions along three mutually perpendicular axes describing the geometries of the small volumes alters the analytical problem. The problems encountered frequently fall into categories which may be classified as requiring a volume probe, a surface probe, or a depth probe analysis. However, in all cases it is of importance to remember that the analysis is being performed on a volume of material containing a specified number of atoms. In addition to analyzing samples of various geometries, an idealized probe analyzer should be capable of handling a range of sample sizes and provide quantitative results over several orders of magnitude in con-

References p. 162

centration for all solids. Chapter IV illustrates the usefulness of the spark source mass spectrograph for the analyses of microsamples. The various ways in which the radio frequency spark source mass spectrograph has been applied to controlled sampling of specified small volumes of various geometries to obtain compositional information will be described in this chapter.

2. APPARATUS

The MATTAUCH–HERZOG double-focusing spark source mass spectrograph used at Westinghouse has been reported previously[7]. The geometry approximates that of the instruments described by HANNAY[11] and GOTO AND KAI[12]. It has a resolving power of about 1 in 500. The spark operates at 800 kc with 20 μsec pulses at a maximum voltage of the order of 30–40 kV. The repetition rate of the 20 μsec pulses can be set for 5, 50, 500, and 5000 cycles/sec. The instrument is equipped with an ion getter pump and a liquid helium cryogenic pump. An additional feature, incorporated into the instrument and used for a number of years, is the step slit monitor electrode. The steps are of equal height and have width ratios of 1, 3, 9, 27, and 81. Thus if the ion beam density is uniform over the entire area, the relative intensity of the ion beams transmitted through the steps will be in the same ratio. Using the photographic plate detector, this arrangement allows the observing at onset of varying intensities in a single exposure. The influence of this arrangement will be seen in the spectra shown. Furthermore, many of the results presented in the work by the authors would not have been detected had we restricted the step aperture to a single aperture of conventional dimensions. The interpretation of the plates by the visual method[13] provides semiquantitative results which are sufficient in most microanalysis work.

3. RESULTS

a. Point to Stationary Plane Configuration

In Fig. 1 is shown a schematic of the mass spectrograph used as a probe in a point to stationary plane configuration. The pointed counter electrode is aligned with the volume to be sampled and separated by a gap spacing of 15 to 25 μ. A high purity gold or silicon point is used. No special emphasis has been placed on the development of techniques for obtaining extremely sharp points in a highly reproducible manner. It is believed that the exact shape of the point is determined by sparking conditions rather than any preassigned geometry. WALLACE AND ROBOZ[14] reported difficulties in attempting to use a sharp point. Commercially available drills (0.0015 in. diameter) have been used in our laboratory with some success as a counter electrode.

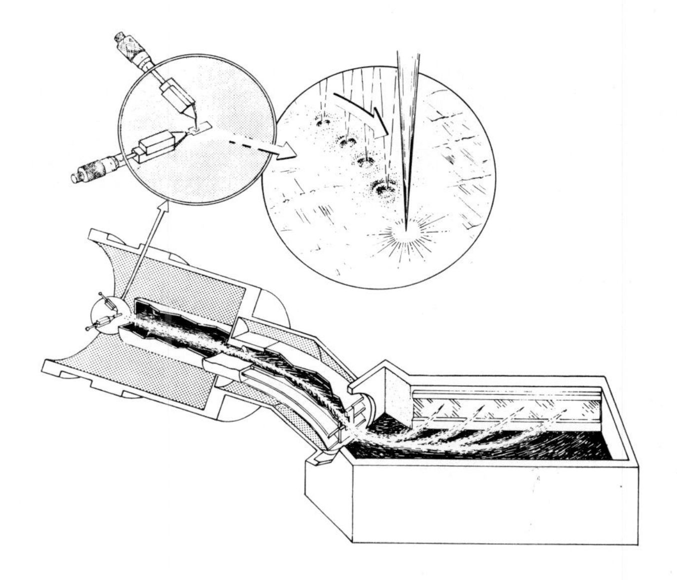

Fig. 1. Mass spectrograph stationary point to plane microprobe schematic.

References p. 162

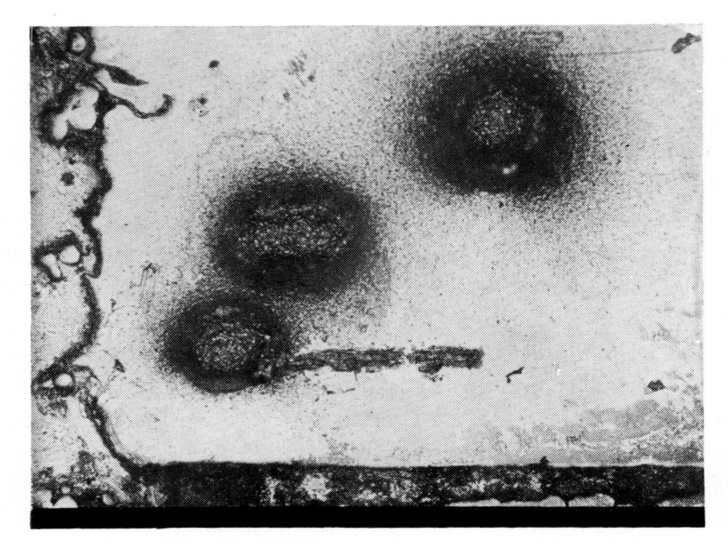

Fig. 2. Mass spectrograph microprobe examination of diffusion couple.

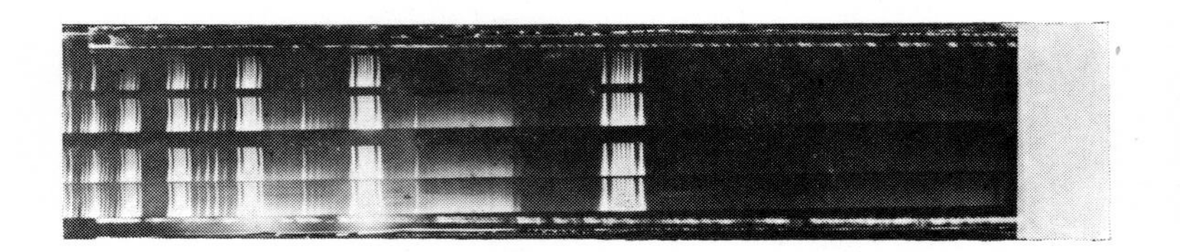

Fig. 3. Mass spectra obtained from molybdenum section of a molybdenum–yttrium diffusion couple.

Fig. 2 is an example of the craters obtained in an investigation of a diffusion couple[15]. The elements yttrium and molybdenum had been heated in contact at elevated temperatures for an extended period of time. The craters were made in order, proceeding from right to left toward the interface. The craters are approximately 100 μ in diameter and 10 μ in depth. The perimeter of the closest crater is approximately 100 μ from the interface. In craters of this magnitude concentrations as low as 1–5 ppm are detected. The spectrum obtained in sampling the molybdenum surface is shown in Fig. 3. No evidence of the presence of yttrium at mass 89 was found. The diameter to depth ratio of craters obtained lies between 8 and 10. This suggests that it would be advantageous to sample an interface in a direction perpendicular to the example just shown since this permits sampling closer to the interface with less chance of contamination. WALLACE AND ROBOZ[14] report the sampling of small volumes in various materials and find craters which are hemispherical. They report craters of diameters of 100–500 μ involving quantities of the order of 1 to 100 μg, and achieve a concentration range of 1 to 100 ppm. The difference in the shape of the craters may be associated with sparking conditions. Their results suggest that they are dealing with larger quantities than we had found necessary in our experiments in order to achieve these concentration levels. Ion extraction from the bottom of a hemispherical crater in a point to plane configuration may be inefficient as compared to extraction from craters having a larger diameter to depth ratio. The shorter path length and lower resolution of our instrument is expected to provide a higher sensitivity. However, many parameters are inadequately defined to draw definite conclusions regarding such differences.

To minimize the size of the craters obtained, we have worked with a so-called "single spark". This appears to the eye as a single spark and consists of a few 20 μsec pulses. An example of the sampling by a single spark from a 0.010 in. diameter iron wire is shown in Fig. 4. This photograph of the resulting crater was obtained with the electron microscope. Both the axis of the wire and the top of the crater were oriented perpendicular to the electron beam of the microscope. The lower photograph shows the buildup at the perimeter of the crater. The crater diameter is 25 μ. The depth of the crater cannot be seen in the photograph but was measured as about 3 μ. The quantity of material removed is of the order of 10^{14} atoms. The mass spectrum obtained contains lines of the iron isotopes 54, 56, 57, and 58. The natural abundance of the 58-isotope is 0.3%. The 3 μ or 30,000 Å depth associated with the crater and a detection limit of the order of 1000 ppm is

References p. 162

Fig. 4. Electron micrograph of crater on 0.01 in. diameter iron wire. (From W. M. HICKAM AND G. G. SWEENEY, *Rev. Sci. Instr.*, 34 (1963) 787).

equivalent to the detection of a 30 Å thick film on an area of $5 \cdot 10^{-6}$ cm^2. The top photograph reveals whisker like growth on the surface outside the perimeter of the crater.

It is interesting to inquire as to what has been the fate of the material piled around the perimeter of the crater, and what would be the fate of it if this sparking had continued. It is believed that this material had been excited many times and redeposited during the course of analysis and that only minor differences in the composition exist between it and the base material. Using known binary alloys as electrodes in the spark source of the mass spectrograph it has been possible to deposit films of the alloys which yield the same mass spectra as that of the starting alloy. In fact, the radiofrequency spark source is a useful tool for depositing films of known atomic composition, and when incorporated into the mass spectrograph allows one to continuously monitor the quantity and composition of such deposited films. Since the atoms originate at a point source, the number of atoms arriving at a unit area per second decreases as r^{-2}.

The use of the mass spectrograph for establishing several impurities in small graphite crystals has been reported[16]. Twelve impurities were identified at concentrations of approximately 1 ppm in 2 mg crystals.

Experiments have been performed on doped films having thicknesses of the order of 3 to 5 μ. The analysis confirms that the sampling is restricted to this depth and that one can achieve detection limits of the order 100–1000 ppm in such cases.

The use of the spark source mass spectrograph within the probe concept has been reported recently[17] regarding detailed distribution of impurities. In this study stationary electrodes were used and the photographic plate was moved in such a manner as to successively record mass spectrum as a function of crater depth. The results relate to changes in elemental composition within the width of a p-n junction and to the distribution of Fe, Si, Cr, Ca, Mo and Cl in rhenium. In the rhenium study, evidence is reported of pairing of the impurities as Ca–Cl, Fe–Cr, and Cr–Si and it is postulated that the impurities exist as either chemical compounds or have identical flow characteristics during crystallization. Mo does not exhibit this behavior.

b. Point to Slowly Translated Plane Configuration

After using the instrument for several years in making analyses of microsamples, it is our conclusion that the technique is as quantitative as it is in dealing with much larger samples. The ability to observe average thicknesses of 30 Å on an area as small as $5 \cdot 10^{-6}$ cm^2 and the semiquantitative nature of the results obtained implies that the information is obtained from a

References p. 162

Fig. 5. Photograph of scanned metallic surface.

sufficiently large number of events to provide satisfactory statistical sampling and excitation. With an increase in the area of sparking by slow translation of the sample with respect to the point, it should be possible to maintain the depth of sampling to the order of 3–5 μ and decrease the average detectable film thickness. Work carried out by manually scanning the surface suggests that this is achieved. An example of the use of this scanning technique with the spark is shown as a strip at the top edge of Fig. 5. Comparison of the original rough fracture surface with the strip reveals that the spark scanning has led to a general smoothing of the surface and a preferential sampling of the high points. Spark excitation of the material associated with a volume having a depth of 3–5 μ and an area of 10^{-4}–10^{-3} cm^2 allows one to detect concentration levels of the order of 1 in 10^4 and an equivalent average thickness of 3–5 Å. AHEARN[18] reported detecting of the order of 0.01 monolayer without difficulty with an instrument of similar geometry.

c. Point to Rotating Plane Configuration

(i) Inorganic

The sensitivity of the scanning method discussed ranks high

among the most sensitive methods used in analysis. Although the method is able to establish concentrations equivalent to monolayers, it lacks in providing information which yields satisfactory spacial identification of the sampled atoms. It is difficult to establish whether the elements observed are present as a film or uniformly dispersed throughout the sampled volume.

In surface and thin film studies, it is highly desirable to specify both the composition and the spacial location to much smaller

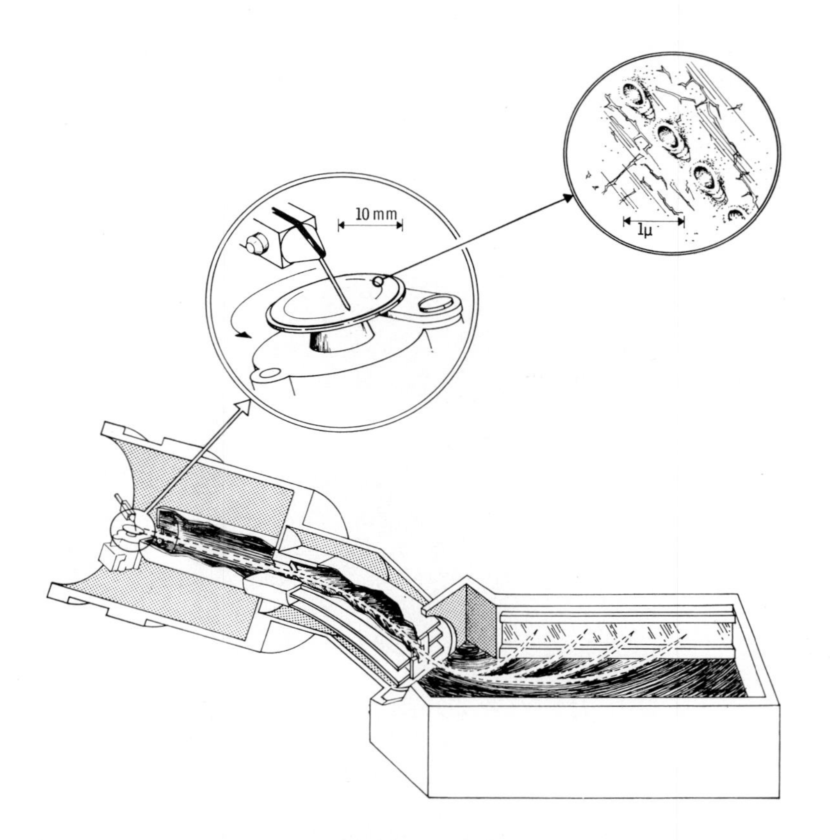

Fig. 6. Mass spectrographic rotating electrode microprobe. (From W. M. HICKAM AND Y. L. SANDLER, *Surface Effects in Detection*, Spartan Books, 1965, p. 193.)

References p. 162

dimensions. A somewhat different approach has been investigated over the past three years in an attempt to satisfy this requirement. The method consists of using a rapidly rotating surface in a point-to-plane configuration[19] in hopes of reducing the sampling depths. Fig. 6 is a schematic illustrating the electrode system. The sample is in the form of a polished disc approximately 2 cm in diameter, which is mounted on a battery operated motor and rotated at 1750 rpm. A stationary point of a noninterfering, high-purity metal is located near the edge of the disc, and less than 25 μ removed from its surface. The linear velocity of the surface with respect to the point is 2 μ per μsec. Both the motor housing and the disc are connected to the ion accelerating voltage supply. High voltage at 800 kc is applied between the point and moving surface from a high ratio step-up transformer.

Fig. 7. Photograph of spinning electrode configuration.

A photograph of the arrangement is shown in Fig. 7. The first ion aperture has been removed in order to show details of the setup. This aperture is supported by the two ceramic insulators shown. In order to accommodate the motor, it was necessary to extend the length of the mass spectrograph envelope. The photograph shows this extension and the mating flanges. The system reverts simply to the conventional, stationary-electrode geometry used in spark source mass spectrometry.

Using a high-purity silicon disc and a gold point, mass spectra were obtained. These contained lines corresponding to silicon, gold, carbon, and oxygen. In short exposures it is estimated that concentrations of the order of 1000 ppm are detectable. In order to establish the influence of sample depth resulting from the high velocity of translation during sparking, the alteration of the polished silicon surface was examined using a scanning microscope. In spite of the mechanical and electrical limitations of this

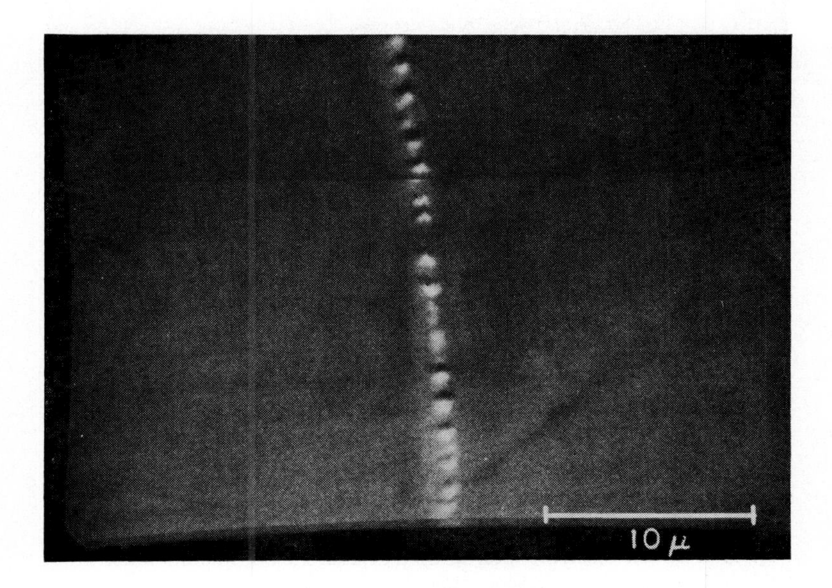

Fig. 8. Scanning electron micrograph of craters on silicon.

References p. 162

experiment, reproducible sampling at radio frequency is achieved as shown in Fig. 8. This scanning electron micrograph covers a track length of 25 μ which represents a time duration of 12 μsec. The track contains 18 distinct craters. The slight curvature observed in the track is the curvature associated with the diameter of the circle at which the track was made. The spacing between the craters corresponds on the average to the time of either one half cycle or one cycle at 800 kc.

In order to observe in greater detail the geometry resulting from

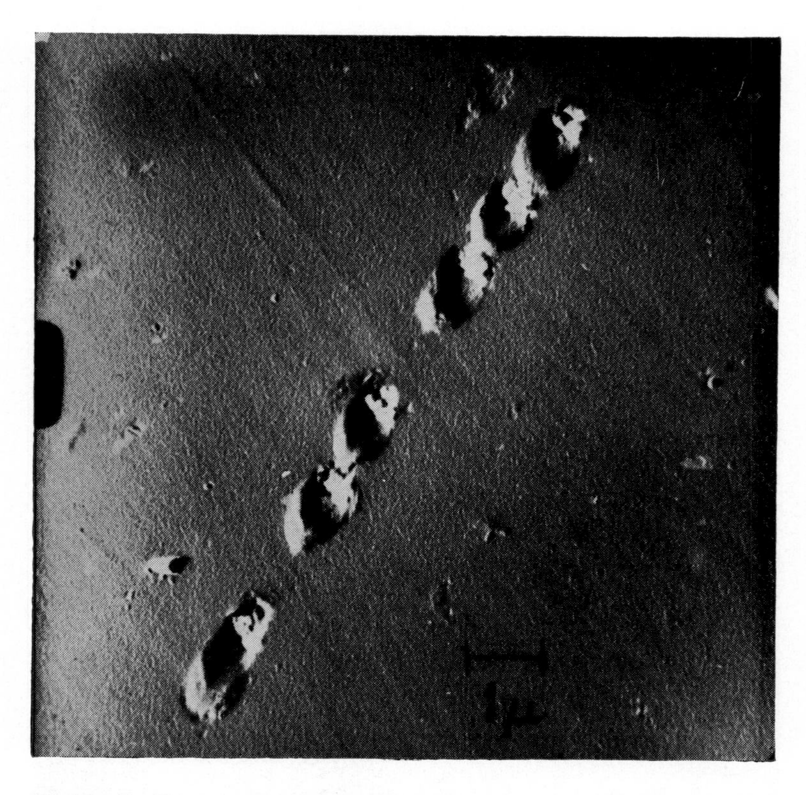

Fig. 9. Replica electron micrograph of craters on silicon, illustrating half cycle and one cycle sampling. (From W. M. HICKAM AND Y. L. SANDLER, *Surface Effects in Detection*, Spartan Books, 1965, p. 194.)

sparking, electron micrograph replicas at higher magnification were made. Fig. 9 is an example of the sampling as observed by this technique. The closely-spaced craters are separated by 1.2 μ in length and 0.6 μsec in time which corresponds to a half cycle at 800 kc sparking frequency. The wider spacing between craters is double the above value and represents firing on a complete cycle. The sample surface was moving from bottom to top during the sparking. Through the use of spheres of known diameter in making the replica and the measurement of the length of the

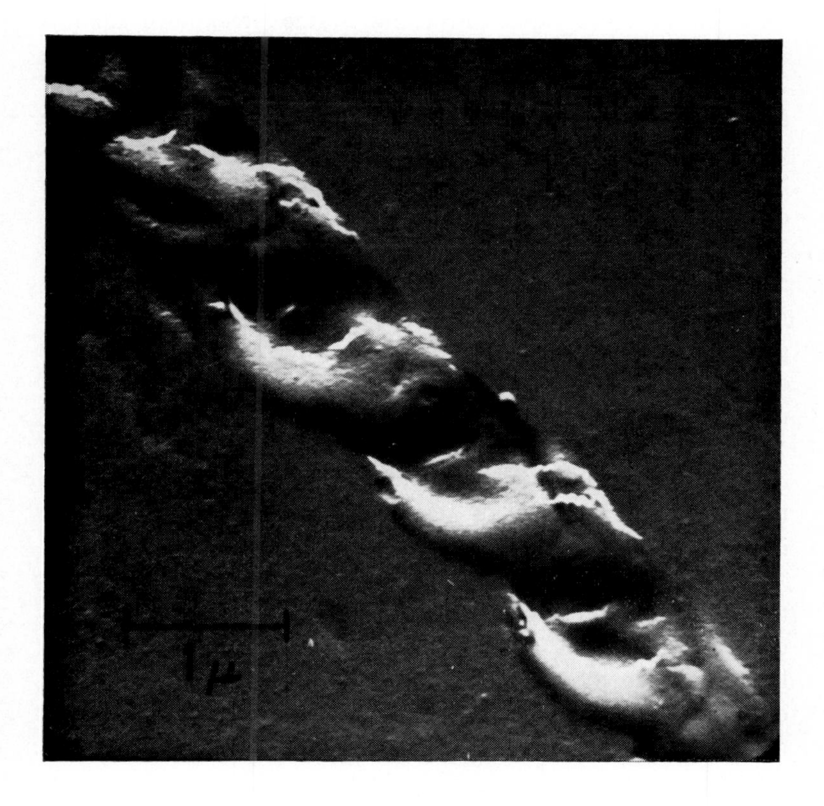

Fig. 10. Replica electron micrograph of craters on silicon illustrating half cycle sampling.

References p. 162

shadow from these spheres as compared to the shadows of the craters, it has been possible to estimate the depth of the crater as being about 2000 Å. The unaltered surface on each side of the two adjoining craters shows in this particular case that firing occurred in one instance on the anode and the other instance on the cathode. FRANZEN[20] has obtained oscillograms showing breakdown only during selected half cycles. HONIG[21] reports a continuous breakdown for several cycles. Both authors had worked with stationary electrodes. The rapid condensation of the vapors by the introduction of a new cool surface at radio-frequency rate is expected to result in more rapid quenching of the breakdown than is achieved with stationary electrodes.

In Fig. 10 is shown an electron micrograph made by the replica technique. This photograph illustrates a continuous chain structure where firing occurs on each half-cycle. The time separation between each of the craters is approximately 0.6 μsec. The width of the entire chain is of the order of 10,000 Å. The similarities of succeeding craters would suggest that the same crater structure results whether the rotating plane is an anode or a cathode.

In Fig. 11 are shown two distinct craters separated by approximately one cycle in time. The photographs suggest that a nearly circular crater is obtained indicating that on this time scale the making of the crater can be associated with a time of less than 10^{-7} sec. The total altered area from a single event is of the order of 2 sq.μ. The crater area is of the order of 0.1 to 0.2 of this total area. The quantity of material associated with each crater is of the order of $6 \cdot 10^{-14}$ g or approximately $1 \cdot 10^{9}$ atoms.

The observed alteration of the surface of the silicon disc suggests that with this configuration sampling is achieved to depths of the order of 2000 Å. In order to better establish that sampling was limited to a depth of this order, thin metallic films were deposited on silicon. The quartz crystal microbalance was used to monitor the quantity of material deposited. The silicon wafers to be coated were placed in the same general vicinity as the crystal balance. On the assumption that both receive material at the same rate, the coating on the silicon disc was computed. A film of copper

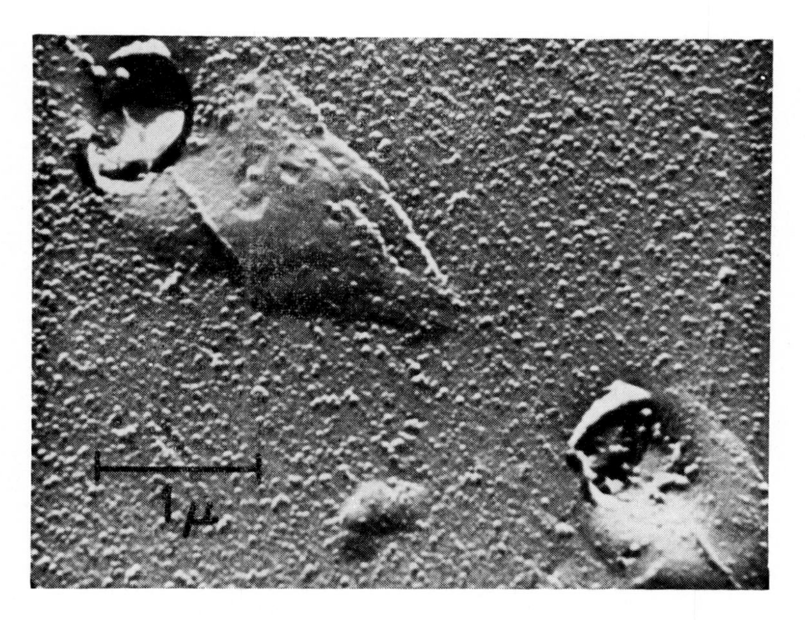

Fig. 11. Individual craters on silicon having diameters of 4000 Å and depths of 2000 Å.

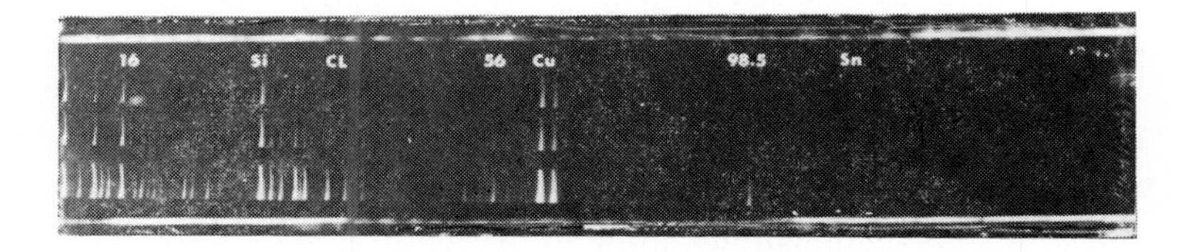

Fig. 12. Mass spectra obtained from a 1000 Å film of copper on silicon using the spinning electrode. (From W. M. HICKAM AND Y. L. SANDLER, *Surface Effects in Detection*, Spartan Books, 1965, p. 195.)

approximately 1000 Å thick was deposited on the silicon. In Fig. 12 is shown a series of three mass spectra obtained from the 1000 Å film on silicon. The intensities of the 63 and 65 isotopes of copper are comparable to the 28 isotope of silicon and suggest that sampling to depths of about 2000 Å is achieved.

References p. 162

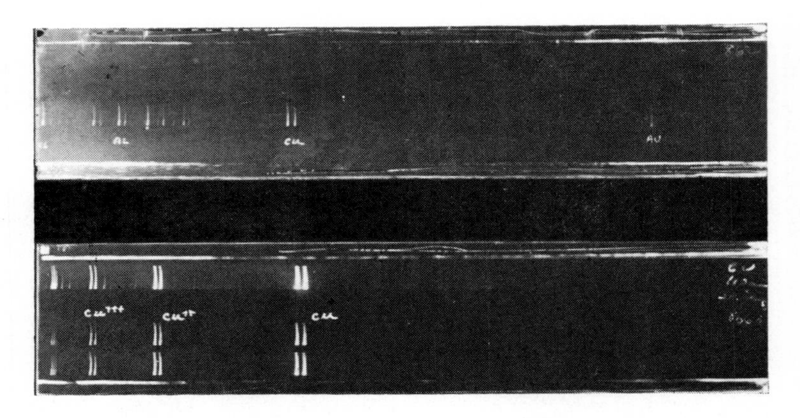

Fig. 13. Mass spectra obtained from polished copper illustrating the variation in surface and bulk composition.

In preparation for etching and for grain size studies, many samples today are polished to a mirror finish in the metallurgical laboratory. A sample of copper was polished to a mirror finish, inserted into the mass spectrograph, and its surface examined using the spinning electrode configuration. Fig. 13 shows the mass spectra obtained on examining the surface with the spinning electrode. The top spectrum reveals aluminum 27 at approximately the same intensity as the 63 and 65 isotopes of copper. The sample had been polished with alumina dust. The three bottom spectra are from the bulk of the same copper wafer from which the top spectrum was obtained and show the absence of aluminum at the 1–5 ppm level.

With the spinning electrode some evidence has been obtained that uniformly distributed elevations of the order of 5000 to 10,000 Å in height can be preferentially analyzed. In the optical examination of metals for carbides, nitrides, and oxides, etching techniques are used to elevate such inclusions above the substrate. Work is in progress to attempt to directly sample such geometrically oriented inclusions in an attempt to analyze these directly with spark source mass spectrometry and observe them at high concentration levels independent of substrate.

The spectrum achieved within the restricted depth of sampling realized with the spinning electrode configuration provides isotopic evidence that concentrations equivalent to a fractional monolayer are detected. In order to obtain such evidence on a system that is reasonably well understood, Langmuir stearate films consisting of a specified number of monomolecular layers on silicon were examined. The technique reveals the presence of Ba in barium stearate films and Cu in copper stearate films of 3–9 monomolecular layers. The results suggest that the system may have wide application in providing information on inorganic and organic lubricants.

(ii) Organics

The study of organic materials with the mass spectrometer[22] has been extremely fruitful. Throughout the years, the molecular weight range of materials examined by this technique has increased. This has led to the development of special high temperature inlet systems in order to reduce degradation of such materials at high temperatures. In order to lessen the time of exposure to the surfaces of such containers, minute furnaces have been placed adjacent to the ion source and electron impact techniques used.

BAUN[23] and co-workers have obtained with the spark mass spectrometer parent molecule ions of a number of organic materials. In the use of the stationary spark, one experiences difficulties that may be associated with a degradation of the sample on prolonged exposure at elevated temperatures in contact with metallic surfaces. Furthermore, polymerization may result in the formation of higher molecular weight materials than the original parent molecule. This in itself can become troublesome in the use of the mass spectra for identification of such organic compounds.

The spinning electrode system provides a means of minimizing some of these difficulties in the analysis of organics. The system serves to bring new undegraded material to the spark at a rate which is compatible with the running frequency of the oscillator. Thus on each half cycle of the spark one is examining original undegraded material. The individual volumes of excited material

References p. 162

in this case may be of the order of 10^{-14} cc. The time associated with the excitation and ionization of the individual volumes is believed to be of the order of a fraction of a microsecond. The transfer distance and the number of wall collisions of the molecules in the vapor state has been reduced in comparison to most vaporization sources employing electron impact. The volume of the high temperature zone under excitation for a single excitation event has been localized. Possibly, during a fraction of the voltage cycle the electric field may be sufficiently high to directly strip an electron from the vaporized molecule as it approaches the electrode surface. In general, mass spectra obtained from this process contain a preponderance of parent molecule ions[24].

One of the materials examined in this manner is phenanthrene, a 3-ring organic compound, $C_{14}H_{10}$, having a molecular weight of 178. This material was prepared in the form of a thin pressed disc. In Fig. 14 is shown a series of mass spectra obtained from the spinning phenenthrene disc. The molecule ion line at mass 178 is among the most intense lines of the spectra. In the bottom spectrum, the disc was maintained stationary during the sparking. One observes a reduction in the intensity of mass 178 relative to the intensity of lines in the C_2 range. This suggests degradation

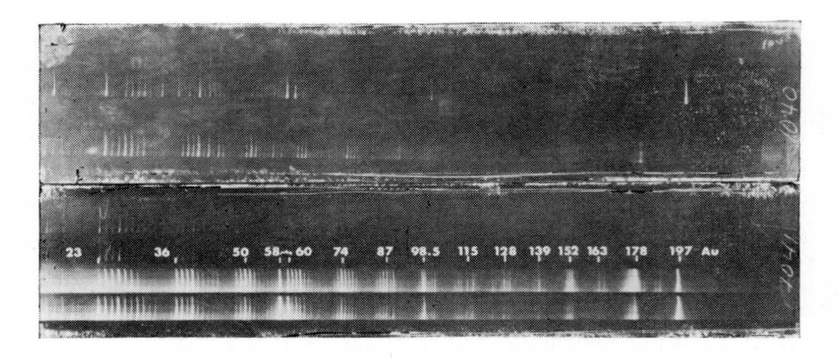

Fig. 14. Mass spectra of phenanthrene obtained by using the spinning and stationary electrode configurations. (From W. M. HICKAM AND Y. L. SANDLER, *Surface Effects in Detection*, Spartan Books, 1965, p. 195.)

Fig. 15. Photograph of phenanthrene disc used in both spinning and stationary configurations.

resulted from prolonged sparking of the same portion of the sample. The point in this case was gold and lines corresponding to this element are present in the spectra. A qualitative comparison of this spectrum with an electron impact spectrum reveals that the intense lines are the same. A photograph of the disc of phenanthrene after sparking is shown in Fig. 15. The paths made from sparking when the disc was rotating are scarcely visible in the photograph. The two black spots are those resulting from sparking under a stationary point-to-plane configuration. This suggests that a large degree of degradation occurs in the use of the stationary electrode as compared to the rotating disc when comparable spectral intensities are achieved. Recently the method has been shown to be useful in analyzing mixtures of anthracene and chrysene and for identification of organic compounds in coal tars[25].

Mass spectrometry has been used to considerable extent for the identification of structural groups within organic molecules. In view of the apparent success of obtaining mass spectra on simple organic molecules, exploratory experiments have been done on more complicated materials. Among the materials examined this way were deoxyribosenucleic acid, identified as DNA, adenine, and cytosine. In DNA the sugar is deoxyribose and the bases are adenine, cytosine, guanine and thymine. The DNA used was from calf thymus. The adenine and cytosine were synthetics. These materials were dissolved in distilled water and a drop of the solution placed on a silicon wafer, which had been slightly roughened by sand blasting to give a more adherent surface. On spinning the wafer, the film uniformly covered the surface of the silicon. The water was then evaporated, leaving a thin film of these materials. Fig. 16 are examples of the mass spectra achieved on DNA, adenine and cytosine. In the DNA spectra, the lines at masses 151 and 152 are tentatively identified as associated with guanine, 135 and 136 associated with adenine, 126 and 127 associated with thymine, and 111 and 112 associated with cytosine. Sodium at mass 23 is the most intense line in the spectrum.

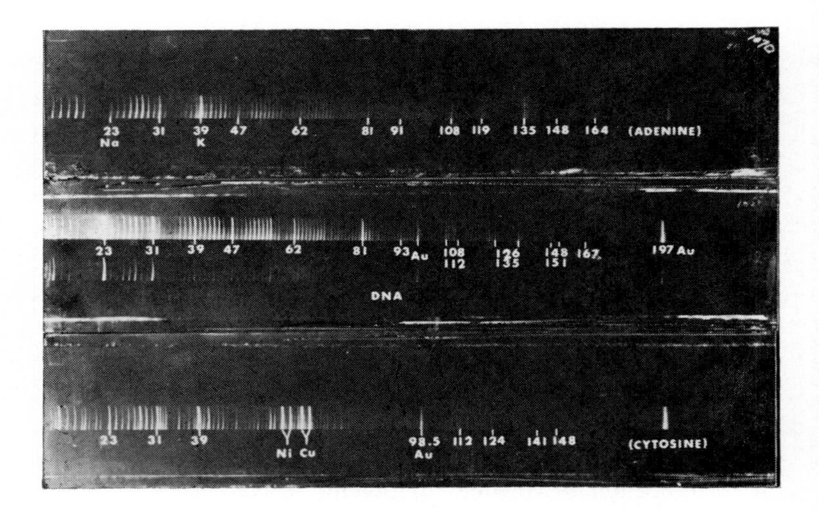

Fig. 16. Mass spectra obtained from films of adenine, DNA, and cytosine using the spinning electrode configuration.

Phosphorus is next, having heavy lines at masses 31, 47, 62 and corresponding to P, PO, and P_2. The mass spectra obtained from adenine contains the 135 and 136 lines corresponding to the parent and parent plus a hydrogen. The lines at masses 31, 47, 62 are due to phosphate and are similar to those found in DNA. The intensity of the line at mass 135 suggests that a considerable amount of the base material is sampled without degradation. The cytosine has a molecular weight of 111. Lines are observed as mass 111 and 112. These preliminary spectra resemble those reported by BIEMANN AND MCCLOSKEY[26] on nucleosides using vaporization followed by electron impact and suggest that the spinning electrode could be useful in the study of complicated organic materials.

4. MASS SPECTROGRAPH FOR NEGATIVE AND POSITIVE IONS

Throughout this book the references to mass spectra have implied positive ion mass spectra. The uniqueness and simplicity of the negative ion spectra of many gases suggests that in future work on solids this aspect should be emphasized. The halogens, carbon, silicon, oxygen and many of the organic materials exhibit negative ion mass spectra. The influence of negative ions on the dielectric strength of gases has been studied[27]. Undoubtedly, the electrical quenching provided by negative ion forming species in the vapor influences the operation of the spark. Since the electron energy dependence of the probability of formation of positive and negative ions is vastly different, the relative abundance of positive to negative ions in the spark discharge may change within a fraction of the radio-frequency voltage cycle. In the investigations of these processes and in the evaluation of the relative merits of the positive and negative ion mass spectra for use in analyzing materials, positive and negative ion mass spectra obtained under the same conditions are needed. The modified MATTAUCH-HERZOG design shown in Fig. 17 makes possible these investigations. This proposed instrument combines the high frequency transmission

References p. 162

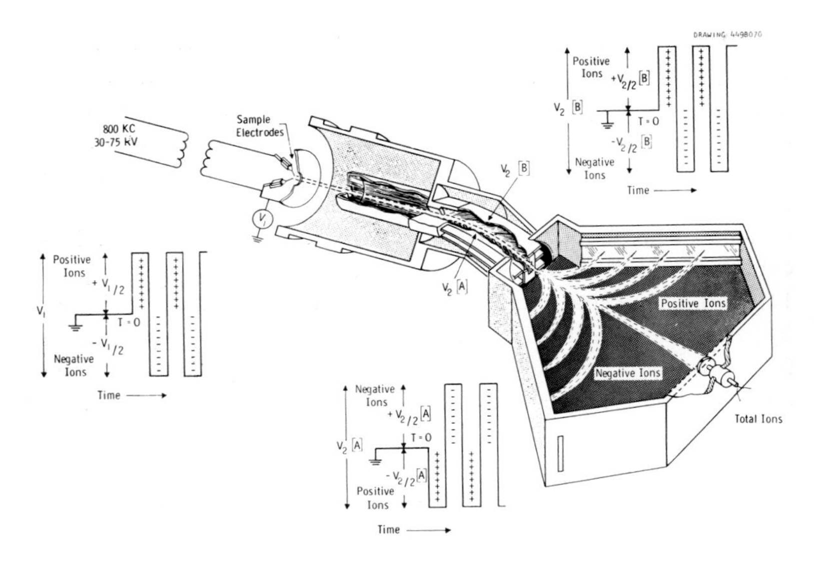

Fig. 17. Mass spectrograph for positive and negative ions.

of alternately positive and negative ions and incorporates a magnetic section which provides mass resolution and recording of both positive and negative ions. All the advantages of the MATTAUCH–HERZOG design, which has been illustrated with numerous examples in this book, have been maintained. The incorporation of the features which allow recording of both positive and negative ion mass spectra recording has been accomplished with little or no increase in the complexity of the system.

Certainly a greater fraction of the future effort in mass spectroscopy of solids should be devoted to negative ion studies than has been in the past. The tremendous influence in many chemical systems of trace quantities of materials known to form negative ions stresses the importance of such work. An instrument of the design proposed could provide a means of exploring this area of study and greatly enhance the field of mass spectroscopy while maintaining continuity of the outstanding progress made in recent years in applying the mass spectrograph to solids. The extention of mass spectrographic techniques to a third state of matter in such a short time would not have been possible without the prior knowledge gained from the wide use of the instrument for gases and liquids.

5. CONCLUSIONS

The developments of the techniques for using the spark source mass spectrograph for microanalysis and in controlled sampling as a microprobe reveal the large potential usefulness of the instrument in this area of analysis. The results reported have been obtained with little modification of instruments built to provide bulk analysis of solids. In order to fully utilize the capabilities of this instrumentation as a microprobe, accessories providing precise positioning and movement of the sample while observed at high magnification are required. Much remains to be done to optimize the sparking conditions for microprobe work and to develop the appropriate electrical components having the desired radio-frequency voltage characteristics. The relative concentration values obtained in analyses are insufficient in fulfilling many of today's materials needs for microanalysis. In the use of the instrument for microanalysis and microprobe analysis, it is demanded that the absolute sensitivity of the instrument be reproducible if reliable analyses are to be obtained since the method is a destructive one. The realization of this condition is expected to improve the quality of the results obtainable when the instrument is used in bulk analyses.

The increase in the acceptance of the instrument as a useful tool for analyzing major constituents, particularly in micro-analyses, somewhat alters the possible concept of an electronic detection system to replace the photographic plate. Suitable electronic detector systems capable of covering concentration ranges of 10^9 to replace the photographic plate may be possible in the distant future. However, if one limits the detector requirement to a concentration range of 10^3, an electronic detector might

References p. 162

be realized in the near future. A particularly attractive feature of the spark source mass spectrometer, in this regard, is that in most analyses a detector range of 10^4 can be expected to cover a concentration range of 10^3. The large range of elemental sensitivities present in many analytical systems requires that the detector range be many orders of magnitude greater than the concentration range of interest.

In analyzing samples over a concentration range as great as 10^9, the requirement of high instrumental resolution in order to reduce the interference encountered has been well documented. In microprobe analysis the detection of concentrations of one part in 10^3 is sufficient frequently and the number of elements involved is greatly reduced. Much of this work can be performed satisfactorily using a smaller, less expensive instrument with a resolution of 1 in 500. Such an instrument would also be useful for determining the concentration of the major constituents in simple alloys.

The frequent bringing together of organic and metallic materials in the same system stresses the need for an analytical technique to span such a range of materials. The results reported on the organic materials with the spinning electrode system suggests that the spark source mass spectrograph may be capable of handling this range of materials. If so, it could contribute to studies in many fields such as catalysis, lubrication, corrosion, and coating techniques. Certainly, the utilization of the instrument in the life sciences in the future years will be an exciting one. Fruitful investigations of these areas can be expected from the use and development of the mass spectrographic microprobe techniques discussed in this chapter.

REFERENCES

1 W. M. Hickam, *Phys. Rev.*, 74 (1948) 1222A; *ASTM Bull.*, 149 (1951) 17.
2 R. E. Honig, *Anal. Chem.*, 25 (1953) 1530; *J. Chem. Phys.*, 22 (1954) 1610.

3 W. A. Chupka and M. G. Inghram, *J. Phys. Chem.*, 59 (1955) 100.
4 R. E. Honig, *J. Appl. Phys.*, 29 (1958) 549.
5 R. Castaing and G. Slodzian, *J. Microscopie*, 1 (1962) 395.
6 R. E. Honig and J. R. Woolston, *Appl. Phys. Letters*, 2 (1963) 138.
7 W. M. Hickam, *Intern. Conf. on Spectroscopy, Univ. of Maryland, 1962*, Paper 50; W. M. Hickam and G. G. Sweeney, *Rev. Sci. Instr.*, 34 (1963) 783.
8 A. J. Dempster, *Proc. Am. Phil. Soc.*, 75 (1935) 755.
9 J. G. Gorman, E. J. Jones and J. A. Hipple, *Anal. Chem.*, 23 (1951) 438.
10 N. B. Hannay and A. J. Ahearn, *Anal. Chem.*, 26 (1954) 1056.
11 N. B. Hannay, *Rev. Sci. Instr.*, 25 (1954) 644.
12 M. Goto and J. Kai, *Mitsubishi Denki*, 33 (1958) 80.
13 R. D. Craig, G. A. Errock and J. D. Waldron, in J. D. Waldron (Editor), *Advances in Mass Spectrometry*, Pergamon, Oxford, 1959, p. 143.
14 R. A. Wallace and J. Roboz, *Annual Conference on Mass Spectrometry, San Francisco, 1963*, Paper 79.
15 W. M. Hickam and G. G. Sweeney, *Annual Conference on Mass Spectrometry, San Francisco, 1963*, Paper 57; A. Taylor, W. M. Hickam and N. J. Doyle, *J. Less-Common Metals*, 9 (1965) 214.
16 W. Fletcher, *Mass Spectrometry Conference, New Orleans, 1962*, Paper 74.
17 G. G. Glavin and V. I. Lyubchenko, *Solid State Phys. (Rus.)*, 7 (1965) 513.
18 A. J. Ahearn, *J. Appl. Phys.*, 32 (1961) 1197.
19 W. M. Hickam and G. G. Sweeney, *Annual Conference on Mass Spectrometry, Montreal, 1964*, Paper 41; W. M. Hickam and Y. L. Sandler in J. I. Bregman and A. Dravnieks (Editors), *Surface Effects in Detection*, Spartan Books, Washington, 1965, pp. 192–196.
20 J. Franzen, *Z. Naturforsch.*, 18a (1963) 410.
21 R. E. Honig, *Annual Conference on Mass Spectrometry, Montreal, 1964*, Paper 38.
22 J. H. Beynon (Editor), *Mass Spectrometry and Its Applications to Organic Chemistry*, Elsevier, Amsterdam, 1960.
23 F. N. Hodgson, M. Desjardins and W. L. Baun, *Tech. Documentary Report No. ASD-TDR-63-383.*
24 M. G. Inghram and R. Gomer, *J. Chem. Phys.*, 22 (1954) 1279.
25 T. Kessler, W. M. Hickam, G. G. Sweeney and A. G. Sharkey, *Annual Conference on Mass Spectrometry, St. Louis, 1965*, Paper 90.
26 K. Biemann and J. A. McCloskey, *J. Am. Chem. Soc.*, 84 (1962) 2005.
27 W. M. Hickam and D. Berg, *J. Chem. Phys.*, 29 (1958) 517.

Name Index

Subject Index